The
Heavy
Frigate

Minerva class 38, 1778 contemporary model.

This fine model of the first purpose-designed 18pdr frigate class is in the Henry Huddleston Rogers Collection of the US Naval Academy at Annapolis. Although the ship was wrongly measured and so is not identified in the existing catalogue, it certainly represents this class, while the iconographical evidence and unique positioning of the hawseholes strongly suggest the *Minerva* herself. The model tallies closely with the draught, except for the quarterdeck barricades being solid; it reflects the initial intentions for the class and should be contrasted with the 'as built' *Arethusa* model from Bristol reproduced later. *(US Naval Academy Museum)*

The Heavy Frigate

Eighteen-Pounder Frigates:
Vol I, 1778-1800

Robert Gardiner

Illustrated with draughts from the collections
of the National Maritime Museum, Greenwich

CONWAY

MARITIME PRESS

© Robert Gardiner 1994

First published in Great Britain in 1994 by
Conway Maritime Press,
an imprint of Brassey's (UK) Ltd,
33 John Street,
London WC1N 2AT

British Library Cataloguing-in-Publication Data
  Gardiner Robert
    Heavy Frigate: 18-pounder Frigates. —
    Vol. 1: 1778-1800 . — (Conway's Ship Types series)
    I. Title II. Series
    623.8

  ISBN 0 85177 627 2

All uncredited illustrations are from the collection of the National Maritime
Museum, Greenwich

Designed and typeset by Fathom Graphics

Printed and bound in Great Britain by the Bath Press, Bath

Contents

Acknowledgements

As THIS IS ESSENTIALLY a sequel to *The First Frigates*, grounded in the same body of long-term research, most of the intellectual debts listed in the earlier book might be justifiably extended to this. However, there are also a number of obligations specific to this book which I am pleased to acknowledge.

The foremost of these is undoubtedly to the Conservation Department of the Public Record Office at Kew. Dr Helen Forde, Head of Preservation, replied both quickly and sympathetically to my request for access to some badly damaged sailing quality reports, taking trouble to fit their conservation into a tightly budgeted programme in order to make them available within my short schedule. Working on the documents themselves was enlivened by the hospitality of Cerina Nichamin and Kate Smith of the conservation workshop who, far from resenting an intruder, were pleased to show me some of the techniques of modern paper preservation. Without sight of these reports, much of this book's design analysis would have been impossible, so the debt is great indeed.

In the search for new illustrations, P W Elkin, the Bristol Museums Curator of Technology, was helpful in procuring prints of their splendid *Arethusa* and *Melampus* models. In this context, it was also a pleasure to work with Bob Sumrall and Major Grant Walker of the US Naval Academy Museum in Annapolis; not only did they supply photographs from their fine collection of ship models, but their willingness to remeasure the ones I found interesting led to the near-certain identification of one as the *Minerva*.

Among a number of readers who wrote to me about *The First Frigates*, there are three who deserve especial thanks for unselfishly supplying additional information from their own researches: Arthur Mack filled in some intriguing background on the first generation of frigates from the Anson correspondence; D J Andrews set me on the track of the Gambier connection (and incidentally supplied some mast and spar dimensions); while from Earl Spencer's papers Richard Saxby came up with the interesting views of Sidney Smith and Lord Bridport which back my thesis that French frigates were not ideal for the strategic duties of the Royal Navy. I would also like to thank the great expert on French warships, Jean Boudriot, for answering some specific queries about the more unusual prize frigates.

The staff of the National Maritime Museum also deserve credit for continuing to find time for researchers while the world of museums undergoes a commercial revolution. David Topliss arranged for me to see a few crucially important original draughts, now located in a remote outstation; the Library staff were courteous and helpful (even on Saturdays, when most of their colleagues had the day off); while the reprographics section struggled manfully with a large print order which included some very obscure subjects – that I did not get all I wanted was not for want of trying.

The book – and the author's confidence – benefited from a reading of the typescript by my old friend David Lyon, but its shortcomings are entirely my own.

ROBERT GARDINER

Introduction

ALTHOUGH THE SAILING NAVY did not formally divide its frigates into light and heavy categories like 1930s Treaty cruisers, the Admiralty and Navy Board frequently referred to 'heavy frigates', a distinction reserved for those more powerfully armed than the 12pdr and 9pdr ships covered in the earlier volume in this series. In later years the term would come to include those with 24pdr guns as well, but there were very few of these before about 1814 and they properly belong in a separate study. The ships covered by this book carried a main armament of twenty-six or twenty-eight 18pdr guns and were first built in small numbers during the American War of Independence. There were a few with thirty 18pdrs but their genesis is closely connected with the 24pdr ships and they have also been omitted, with a view to a future volume on the big frigates.

No more 12pdr ships were designed after 1783 and the relative importance of the 18pdr frigate in the fleet grew rapidly, so that by 1800 they outnumbered 12pdr ships on the Navy List. For this reason they may be regarded as the standard cruising ship of the French Revolutionary and Napoleonic Wars. The success of the big American frigates in the War of 1812 suggested to some navies that the days of the 18pdr-armed frigate were over, but the traditional British requirement for large numbers of cruising ships meant that the Royal Navy continued to build such ships down to the major reorganisation of the naval administration in 1832.

Because of the policy of building small numbers of many designs during the 1790s, it has been necessary to divide the 18pdr ships into two volumes in order to do justice to the complex origins of all the various classes. To the general historian the Peace of Amiens (1802) might seem a logical break-point, but in terms of ship design the end of Lord Spencer's relatively long period at the Admiralty is far more significant. When St Vincent's Board took over in February 1801 it was to alter radically both the type of ships required and the manner in which they were ordered. The last frigate contract while Spencer was First Lord was placed late in 1800 and it marks the end of the coverage of British frigates in this volume; changes in shipbuilding policy, on the other hand, had no influence on captured vessels so it seemed more logical to include all the prizes down to the end of hostilities in 1801.

The Danish *Pommern*, 36 guns, ex-Swedish *Illerim*, as refitted 1741.

The first recorded example of an 18pdr-armed single-decked cruiser was this
large Swedish commerce raider built in 1716. She carried twenty-four 18pdrs
on the main deck and twelve 8pdrs on the upperworks. It is not clear if the
ship was 'frigate-built' with a complete lower deck, but, as with many later
Swedish cruisers, the captain's accommodation was on the quarterdeck
rather than under it. As can be seen by the date of this draught, the ship
enjoyed a long career in the Danish navy following capture, and such was the
reputation of the ship that the Swedes built a similar ship of the same name
as late as the mid-century. *(Rigsarkivet, Copenhagen)*

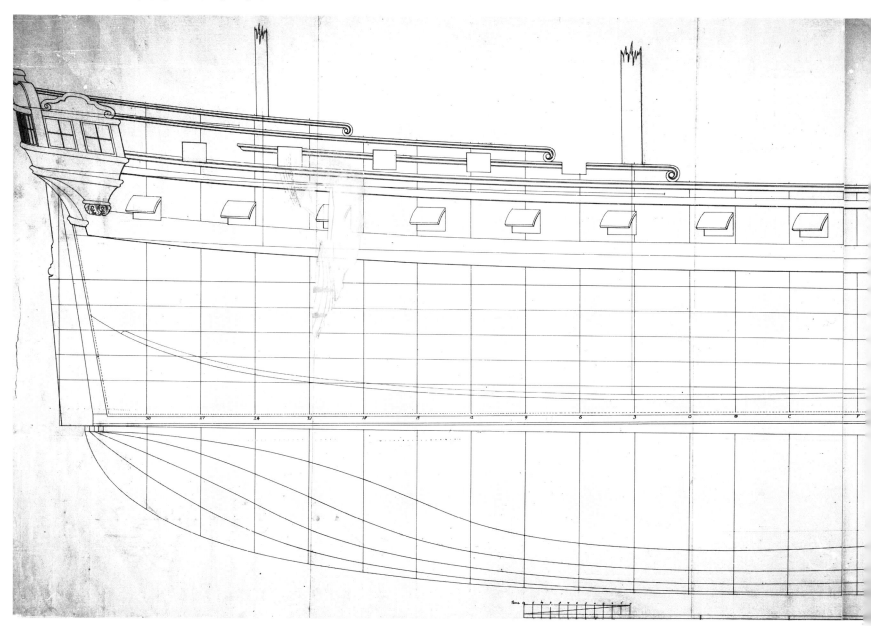

Part I: Design History

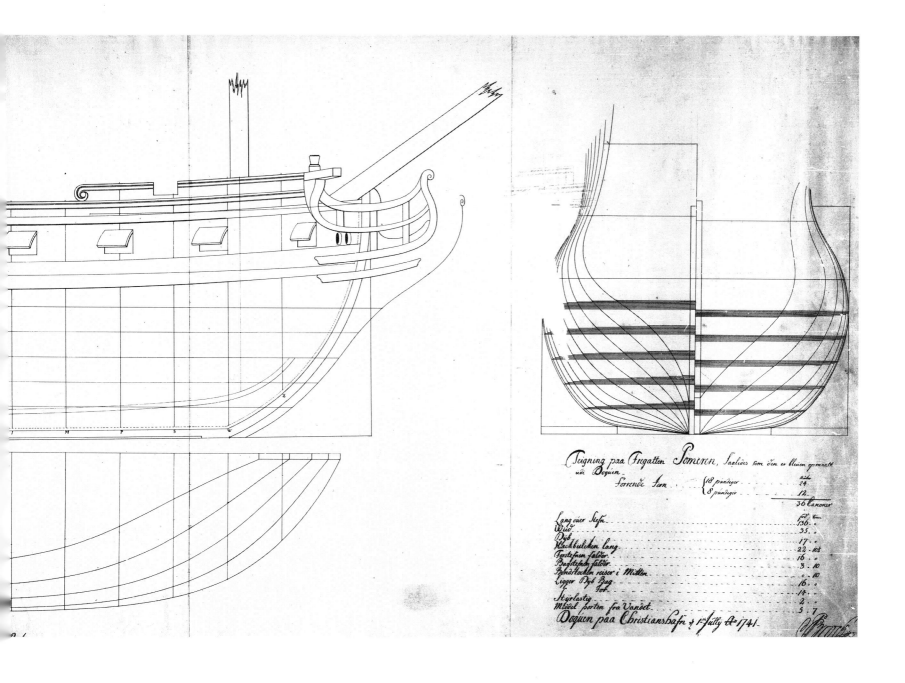

1. The Prehistory of the 18pdr Cruiser

From its gradual evolution at the end of the seventeenth century, the specialist cruising ship was marked not only by fewer guns than line of battle ships but also by weapons of lighter calibre. The reasons for this were perfectly logical: whereas battleships were designed for firepower and structural strength to withstand the battering they would endure in the line of battle, cruisers were optimised for speed and seakeeping. Their duties of fleet reconnaissance and trade warfare required guns capable of dealing only with similar enemy vessels, privateers and armed merchantmen.

A smaller number of bigger guns was ruled out by three factors: the heavy hull construction required by the larger calibres would militate against good sailing qualities; a small ship was a lively gun platform, making it difficult to handle large guns in any kind of seaway; and the slow rate of fire from relatively few guns reduced the chances of scoring enough hits to do real damage. Attempts were made at compromise, and the half-battery ships built in the 1690-1715 period[1] carried a few heavier guns on a partially armed lower deck, but even these were only 9pdrs (although France built some with 12pdrs). Their value was limited since the low freeboard of the gunports meant that they could only be used in good weather, a restriction that also applied to small two-deckers like the English 40/44-gun ships that were often employed as cruisers. For all practical purposes, with a ship heeling to leeward, only the weather-side guns could be counted on, which suggests that these ships were tactically defensive: *ie* likely to take up the leeward station, in situations such as convoy defence or when attacked by a superior opponent.

By the early eighteenth century it came to be accepted that proper cruising ships needed only a single gundeck, but one sufficiently far from the waterline to be usable in all weathers. For stability reasons the armament weight had to be kept down and as a result a genuine cruiser could almost be defined by its lower ratio of firepower to tonnage.[2] For the first half of the eighteenth century most single-deckers carried 6pdrs or 9pdrs (with 12pdrs in the lower batteries of small two-deckers) and any increase in calibre could only be achieved by a disproportionate increase in the size of ship – in effect to further reduce the firepower ratio, as occurred when frigate-form ships began to replace small two-deckers in the 1740s.[3]

For most countries, abnormally large – and hence costly – cruisers could not be justified, but there were isolated attempts to introduce such ships, and one remarkable example that came to fruition. This last, the Swedish *Illerim* of 1716, was no less remarkable in its origins than its design. The final stages of the Great Northern War (1699-1719) saw the Swedes, outnumbered at sea by their Danish and Russian opponents, waging a trade war so indiscriminate that it threatened Britain's

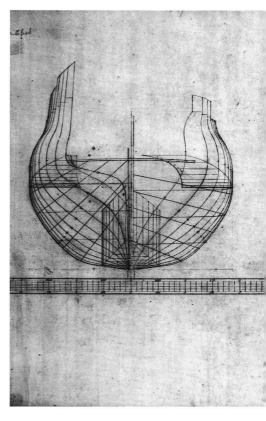

Unidentified sheer draught of a 40-gun ship, ?1757.

This previously unidentified draught may represent Captain Shirley's proposal for a 40-gun frigate armed with twenty-eight 18pdrs. The draught has the requisite number of upper deck ports, which are large enough for 18pdrs, and more than the necessary twelve ports on the upperworks for the secondary guns (this excess was common in cruising ships so is not significant). Stylistically, the draught seems to date from the early Slade era, including some apparent confusion about whether the ship is to have a round bow or beakhead, and which deck the hawseholes will enter. These concerns are typical of the period 1755-58, so even if this is not Shirley's own draught – and it has many features of Admiralty draughting – it may represent Slade's working up of Shirley's concept.

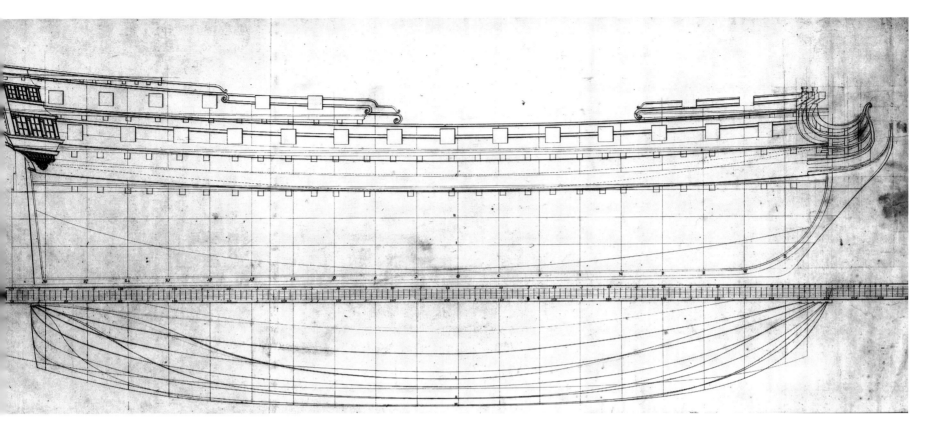

Baltic trade - and in particular naval stores. Consequently a powerful Royal Navy fleet was sent to co-operate with the allies in the years from 1715, further reducing the possibilities of fleet action for the Swedish navy. With the Baltic swarming with enemy vessels, even commerce warfare was a dangerous prospect and a series of particularly powerful cruisers was designed in response.

These were believed to be the product of direct intervention by Sweden's despotic and warlike King Charles XII, who even ordered the navy to consider cruisers armed with 24pdrs. The naval ministry persuaded him that this was not practical, but four big single-deckers were built, the largest being the *Illerim*, which carried twenty-four 18pdrs on the main deck. The rationale was simple: the ship could outfight any likely escort or even take on two-deckers in heavy weather when they could not open their lower deck ports; failing this, she could escape by superior sailing. However, history offers many examples of the tactical futility of the individual super-ship concept,[4] and *Illerim* was taken while nearly new by a force of British cruisers in October 1716. She made no discernible impact on her captors, who turned the ship over to the Danish navy, with whom, as the *Pommern*, she enjoyed a long career. Despite her short service life, in Sweden the ship was highly regarded and a replacement vessel of the same name and similar design was built in the middle of the century.

A large cruiser is usually the product of strategically defensive thinking, particularly appealing to navies who do not expect to command the seas (the ultra-fast steam frigates of the American

Wampanoag type are a nineteenth-century example). Therefore it is not surprising that France should have toyed with such concepts from time to time. In November 1762 the Assistant Constructor at Brest, Lamothe, proposed a big frigate armed with thirty 18pdrs and twenty 8pdrs, with dimensions of 145ft x 37ft x 19ft French measure. With a gunport freeboard of 7½ft, they would have been all-weather ships, of far superior sailing qualities to the old half-battery 40/46-gun ships, and better value than the 50-gun two-deckers they would effectively replace. Lamothe envisaged about a dozen such vessels playing havoc with British trade, as they were more than a match for any likely convoy escort. These would have been costly ships and with the Seven Years War coming to its disastrous conclusion for France his proposal was not followed up, but he made one further – and equally abortive – attempt to interest his government in a slightly reduced version in 1769.[5]

Curiously, Britain had already considered and rejected a similar vessel. In June 1757 one Captain Shirley submitted a plan of a 40-gun frigate to be armed with twenty-eight 18pdrs and twelve 9pdrs or 6pdrs. There is an unidentified draught in the Admiralty Collection which agrees with the main features of this design and is stylistically correct for the period; if this is indeed Captain Shirley's proposal, then the vessel would have been about 146ft x 37ft, very close in size to Lamothe's revised design. The Navy Board may have given it serious consideration but it was returned to the Admiralty with the curt observation that designing ships 'is the proper province of the Surveyor'. The Admiralty informed Shirley that 'Their Lordships do not think it proper to

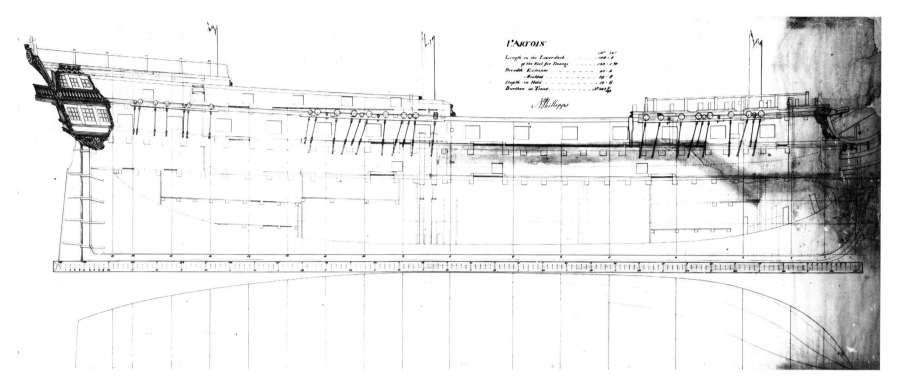

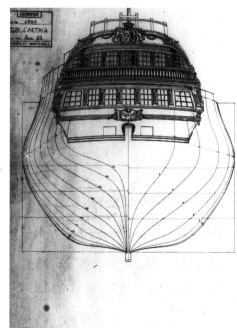

Artois, 40 guns, ex-French, as captured sheer & profile draught, 1780.

The 18pdr frigate first entered French service in the form of this large privately-built ship. The elaborate quarterdeck accommodation and the small loading ports on the lower deck give the ship the appearance of an East Indiaman, although she has relatively sharp lines. The ship was to play a notable part in the development of carronades: she was one of their first victims, and the effectiveness of *Bienfaisant*'s 12pdr carronades in suppressing her small arms fire during the action in which she was captured was much quoted; in British service the ship carried out a number of important experiments with what was still a new weapon, including mounting the first 68pdrs to go to sea.

introduce any new practice' at the present time,[6] thus expressing the traditional British reluctance to force the pace of naval development. Having only just introduced the 12pdr frigate, which was considered an adequate replacement for the old two-decked 44, there was no reason to take another leap in dimensions and cost, particularly as there was no obvious role for such a ship in British strategy.

French designers returned to the concept of a large commerce raider with J M B Coulomb's November 1775 memorial. These vessels would be too large for fleet duties but would be ideal for trade warfare, and while they would carry 12pdrs in peacetime so as not to strain the hull, they would be built strong enough to take twenty-six 18pdrs in war (plus ten 8pdrs). There is also a further report lobbying for 18pdr ships from a M Pinet in July 1778, but his exact status is unclear;[7] what is certain is that the French navy did not act on any of these proposals, because no 18pdr frigate was being laid down until 1781. For once it was left to the British to make the definitive move.

2. *Britain Adopts the 18pdr, 1778*

In the early years of the war in North America, the special circumstances of the struggle with the colonies led the Admiralty to concentrate on a building programme consisting of 28-gun Sixth Rates and a few 44-gun ships. At first the colonists had no real navy, but the British army's long transatlantic supply lines were vulnerable to American privateers. The 28s were a match for the vast majority of these, and their relatively shallow draught made them more useful than larger cruisers in the coastal operations that marked the opening stages of the conflict. The 44s provided a cheap local 'ship of force', and with 18pdrs on the lower deck, were far more powerful than any likely opponent.

The building of the first American frigates in 1776 had no impact on British construction policy, since there were already more than enough 32s to cope. Because of the problems of finding suitable armament,

Minerva class 38, 1778 contemporary model.

A quarter view of the Annapolis model. The long, solid barricade reflects a later modification; this is shown on the draughts of the later ships, but was probably incorporated into *Minerva* before commissioning in order to accommodate the carronades established in September 1779. The model does not have oarports, like the *Minerva* draught, whereas the later ships do. *(US Naval Academy Museum)*

Table 1: *MINERVA* CLASS 38-GUN FIFTH RATES Specification

Armament:	Upper deck	Quarterdeck	Forecastle	Guns	Men
Design	28 x 18pdrs	8 x 6pdrs	2 x 6pdrs	38	270
Changes by AO:					
30 Sep 1779 added		6 x 18pdr carr	4 x 18pdr carr		
		14 x $\frac{1}{2}$pdr swivels			
25 Apr 1780		All 6pdrs replaced with 9pdrs			280
Designed by Sir Edward Hunt					

	Lower deck	Keel	Breadth extreme	Depth in hold	Burthen
	ft-ins	ft-ins	ft-ins	ft-ins	tons
Design	141-0	117-0$\frac{3}{8}$	38-10	13-9	938^{72}/$_{94}$
As completed					
Minerva	141-0	117-0$\frac{3}{8}$	38-10	13-9	940
Arethusa	141-1$\frac{1}{2}$	116-10$\frac{5}{8}$	39-0$\frac{1}{2}$	13-9$\frac{1}{2}$	948
Phaeton	141-0	116-5$\frac{1}{4}$	39-0$\frac{1}{2}$	13-10$\frac{1}{4}$	944
Thetis	141-6	117-1$\frac{1}{8}$	39-1$\frac{1}{2}$	13-8	954

Notes:

The last two ships were built to very slightly modified lines.

*Melampu*s, 36, was originally ordered to this design.

The carronades ordered in Sep 1779 conformed to the Jul 1779 establishment but in Jul 1782 *Arethusa* carried 4 and 2 x 18pdr carr on the quarterdeck and forecastle, while *Minerva* had only 4 x 18pdr carr on the quarterdeck; both *Phaeton* and *Thetis* seem to have been completed without any carronades.

Armament of the upperworks from 1793 onwards is listed in Table 60.

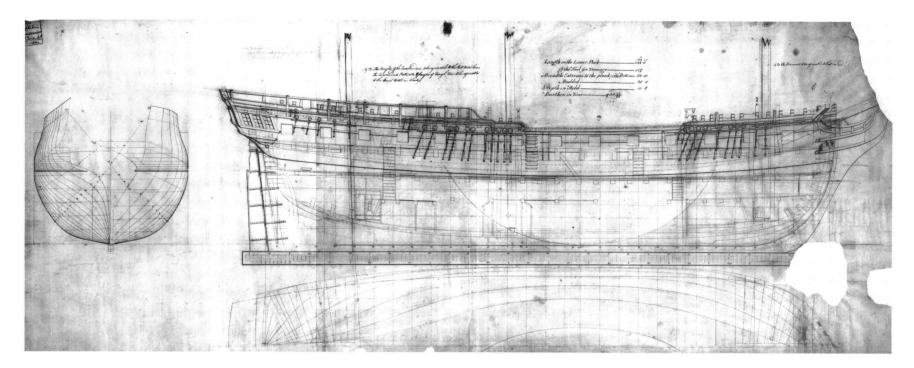

some American ships had odd batteries, including some 18pdrs – *Warren*, for example, had a mixed batch of 18pdrs and 12pdrs on her upper deck and the *Alliance* of 1777 is reputed to have carried twenty-eight 18pdrs. These developments were too small and piecemeal to concern the Admiralty, but French entry into the war in 1778 was a different matter. New 32s (and, incidentally, 74s) were put in hand immediately, but the first few months of open warfare provided no single-ship successes against French frigates. Indeed, the *Belle-Poule* put up surprising resistance when set upon by the *Arethusa* (which had the whole of Keppel's Channel Fleet in support).

Although only 12pdr-armed, the French frigates of this era were very large – some over 900 tons and over 140ft long, compared with the standard British 32 of about 680 tons and 126ft. Two vessels, the *Indiscrète* and *Sensible* built at Nantes in 1766, carried twenty-eight upper deck guns and the even larger *Terpsichore* and *Renommée* had thirty; *Concorde* had just been completed and three other vessels with twenty-eight ports were to follow shortly.[8] In a war in which the Royal Navy might find itself outnumbered for once, the Admiralty was anxious not to be outgunned as well. On 21 October 1778 the Admiralty directed the Navy Board to propose no more frigates under 32 guns, but also to consider the possibility of 36- or 38-gun frigates capable of carrying twenty-eight 12pdrs and 6pdrs on the upperworks.

The Navy Board replied on the 29th with a counter proposal, arguing that frigates of the size contemplated should be built with the scantlings strong enough to carry 18pdrs, and enclosed draughts of a 36 and a 38. There are other examples of frigate draughts being produced in a week but they are rare, and it is more likely that, knowing the trend of Admiralty thinking, the Surveyors had already done the preparatory work. Charles Middleton (later Lord Barham) had joined the Navy

Minerva, **38 guns, 1778, design sheer & profile draught.**

The draught is not particularly well finished, which may be a sign of haste, and some second thoughts are annotated: the fore mast was moved aft slightly, and the height of the quarter-deck rails and depth of the port sills were altered. This ship differed from her sisters in the positioning of the hawseholes between the cheek pieces; in the later ships they were moved above the upper cheek.

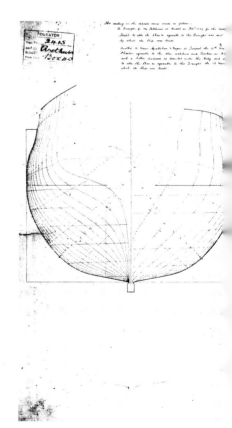

Arethusa, **38 guns, 1779, design sheer & profile draught.**

The second ship of the class incorporated some minor modifications, including moving the hawseholes up above the upper cheek, adding oarports, and a longer, solid barricade. A note on the draught points out that a modified sheer was sent to the builders in December 1780 from which the ship was built. More importantly, another note mentions the modified lines used for *Phaeton* 'agreeable to the stern waterlines and timbers in black ticked lines with a hollow deadwood as described under the body and a sketch to alter the sheer as agreeable to this draught the 19 March 1781 by which the ship was built.' *Thetis* was similar to *Phaeton* in these respects.

Table 2: *MINERVA* CLASS 38-GUN FIFTH RATES
Building Data

Name	Ordered	Builder	Laid down	Launched	Sailed	Fitted at	Fate
Minerva	6 Nov 1778	Woolwich Dyd	Nov 1778	3 Jun 1780	6 Jul 1780	Woolwich	1798 renamed *Pallas*, troopship; Mar 1803 BU
Arethusa	26 Jan 1779	Hilhouse, Bristol	23 Aug 1779	10 Apr 1781	1 Jun 1781	Bristol	May 1815 BU
Phaeton	3 Mar 1780	Smallshaw, Liverpool	Jun 1780	12 Jun 1782	Dec 1782[1]	Plymouth	26 Mar 1828 sold for BU
Thetis	22 Sep 1781	Randall, Rotherhithe	Dec 1781	23 Sep 1782	15 Nov 1782	Deptford	9 Jun 1814 sold

Notes:

[1] *Phaeton* left Liverpool for Plymouth in Oct 1782 for fitting.

Board as Comptroller a few months previously and he was a lifelong advocate of improvements in ship design[9] so even if the initiative was not his he is likely to have been a strong supporter of such a development. The covering letter claimed that 'Such frigates we conceive will exceed in strength any now possessed by the French and may be constructed with every advantage that such ships ought to have.'[10]

The Admiralty usually took instant decisions when approving draughts but took a few days to consider the new designs before ordering one 36 (*Flora*) to Sir John Williams' design, and one 38 (*Minerva*) to a draught by the junior Surveyor, Sir Edward Hunt, on 6 November. The ships represented a substantial increase in the unit cost of cruisers, and as befits the prototypes of an important new ship type, both were allocated to Royal Dockyards, where quality could be assured and any problems thrown up by their novelty could be more easily and quickly resolved.

Since Anson's time at the Admiralty in the mid-1750s it had been the custom to have each of the two Surveyors produce a competing design to a common specification for every major new class, and in 1779 Hunt came up with a new 36 (which became the *Perseverance* class) and Williams another 38 (the *Latona*). In theory this system allowed a comparison to be made and the better design could then be built in numbers. However, in practice this was not always the case and Middleton, who tried to have the joint Surveyorship abolished in 1781, believed it 'must unavoidably occasion jealousy, difference in opinion, and obstruct the public service'. He went on to say that it it only worked

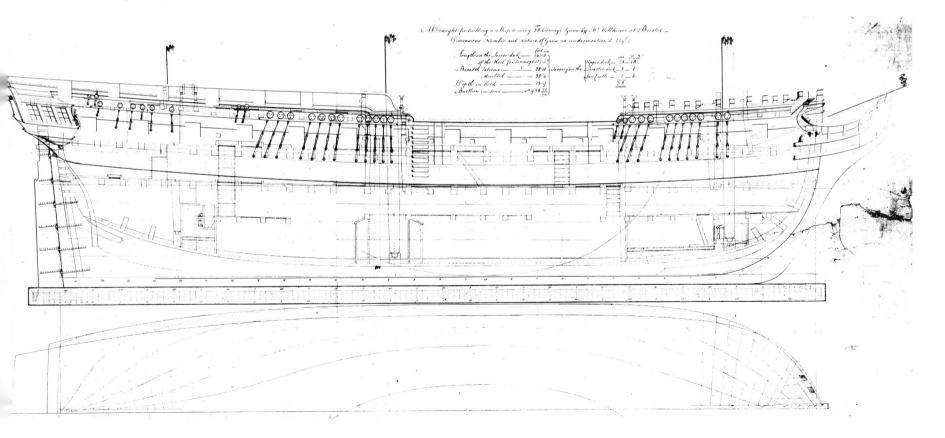

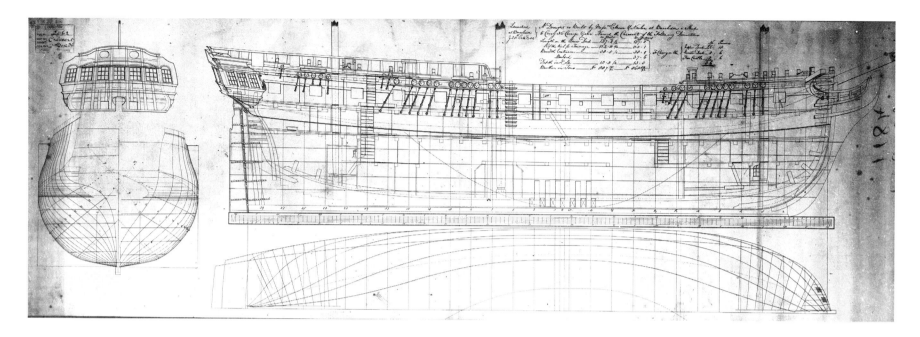

Table 3: *LATONA* CLASS 38-GUN FIFTH RATE
Specification

Armament:	Upper deck	Quarterdeck	Forecastle	Guns	Men
Design	28 x 18pdrs	8 x 6pdrs	2 x 6pdrs	38	270
Changes by AO:					
30 Sep 1779 added		6 x 18pdr carr	4 x 18pdr carr		
		14 x ½pdr swivels			
25 Apr 1780		All 6pdrs replaced with 9pdrs			280
Designed by Sir John Williams					

	Lower deck	Keel	Breadth extreme	Depth in hold	Burthen
	ft-ins	ft-ins	ft-ins	ft-ins	tons
Design	141-0	116-7	38-10	13-6	933
As completed					
Latona	141-3	116-10	38-11¾	13-6	944

Notes:

On 14 Nov 1782 the Admiralty ordered the Navy Board to contract with Fisher of Liverpool for a second vessel of this class but it never came to fruition.

The carronades ordered in Sep 1779 conformed to the Jul 1779 establishment, but in Jul 1782 ship carried only 4 x 18pdr carr on the quarterdeck besides the long guns.

The armament of the upperworks from 1793 is listed in Table 60.

Crescent, Flora class 36, as built(?) sheer & profile draught, 1784.

The *Flora* class, the first 18pdr 36, was designed at the same time as the first 38s and shared many aspects of the basic layout. This draught depicts one of the later ships of the class and quotes both launch date and as built dimensions, but shows no more detail than a design draught. The armament lists 6pdrs, which had been changed to 9pdrs long before this ship was completed, so this is either a tracing of the design draught or the original to which the 'as completed' details were added later.

at all because of the 'good-natured disposition of Sir John Williams and the attention of Mr Hunt to his infirmities'.[11] To avoid personalities, it was common to continue building both designs long after the prototypes had gone to sea, and this pattern can be seen in the orders for the 36s, which alternate exactly between the *Flora* and *Perseverance* classes.

Initially the 38s were given higher priority, with four on order by mid-1780 compared with two 36s. The second 38, the *Arethusa*, was ordered a few months after *Minerva*, and by the joint system should have been to a new Williams design, but was actually a repeat of the prototype. It is possible that Williams' 'infirmities' were beginning to make their mark, and he certainly did not complete his new draught until six weeks later, which was then used for the *Latona*. This was to be his only 38,[12] but if this suggests any particular judgement on Williams' design it was part

Table 4: *LATONA* CLASS 38-GUN FIFTH RATE
Building Data

Name	Ordered	Builder	Laid down	Launched	Sailed	Fitted at	Fate
Latona	23 Mar 1779	Graves & Purnell, Limehouse	Oct 1779	13 Mar 1781	21 Apr 1781[1]	Deptford	1813 hulked; 2 May 1816 sold

Notes:

[1] Sailed to Deptford for fitting 15 Mar 1781.

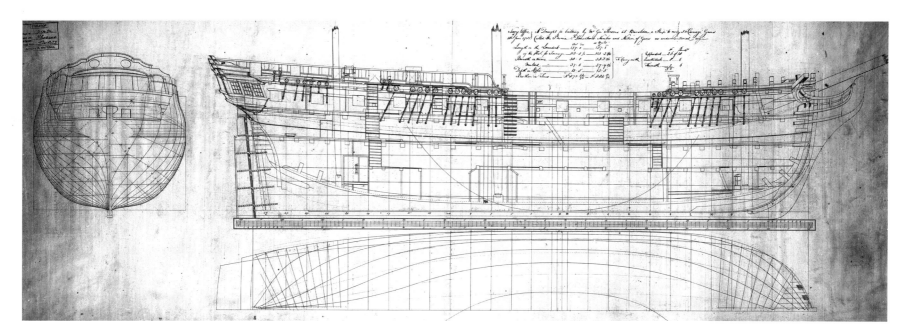

Phoenix, Perseverance class 36, design sheer & profile draught, dated 18 June 1781.

Hunt's 36-gun design was very similar to, if a little sharper than, the Williams parallel design. One distinguishing feature was the slightly longer quarterdeck rails of the *Perseverance* class.

Latona, 38 guns, design sheer draught, dated 23 March 1779.

Williams's equivalent of the *Minerva* class was confined to a single ship. As with the contemporary 36s, the two designs were very similar in dimensions and layout, and even the hull forms were not radically different. This draught shows the original pristine concept of the upperworks, with light rails for the proposed 6pdrs and swivel stocks, before carronades were contemplated. Like the *Minerva*, the draught shows no oarports.

of a general lack of confidence in his abilities after about 1780.[13]

In fact only two more 38s were ordered after the middle of 1780 (one of which was converted to a 36 during construction) compared with six 36s laid down as such. Curiously, the two-decked 44-gun ship continued to have its supporters in the administration and this was one among the many technical issues on which Middleton corresponded with Rear-Admiral Richard Kempenfelt. The latter was well-read, considered in his judgements, and a keen advocate of improvements in many aspects of naval warfare.[14] Kempenfelt consulted other officers and found a unanimous opinion in favour of the 38, which seemed superior on virtually every count, which he listed as follows:

1. There was virtually no difference in nominal firepower [Kempenfelt

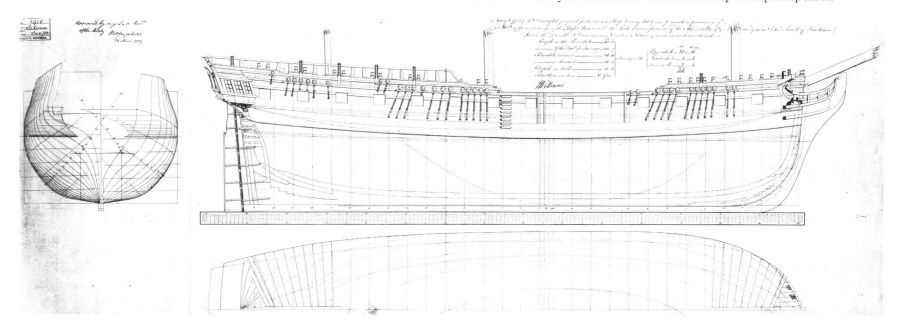

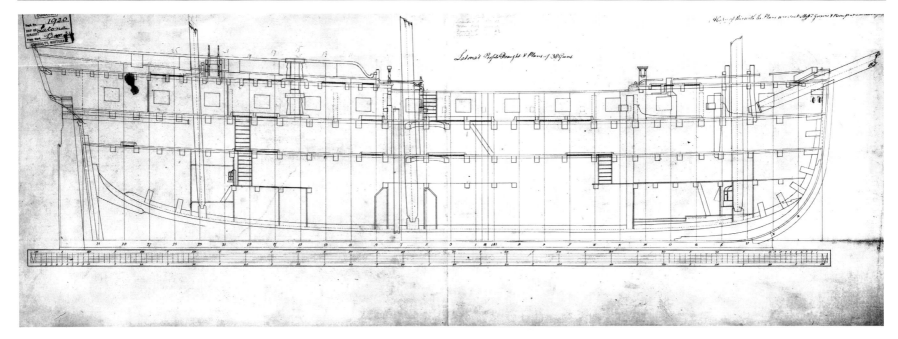

Latona, 38 guns, design profile draught, dated 15 July 1779.

Table 5: *FLORA* CLASS 36-GUN FIFTH RATES
Specification

Armament:	Upper deck	Quarterdeck	Forecastle	Guns	Men
Design	26 x 18pdrs	8 x 6pdrs	2 x 6pdrs	38	260
Changes by AO:					
30 Sep 1779 added		4 x 18pdr carr	4 x 18pdr carr		
		12 x ½pdr swivels			
25 Apr 1780		All 6pdrs replaced with 9pdrs			270
Designed by Sir John Williams					

	Lower deck	Keel	Breadth extreme	Depth in hold	Burthen
	ft-ins	ft-ins	ft-ins	ft-ins	tons
Design	137-0	113-1	38-0	13-3	869
As completed					
Flora	137-0	113-1	38-0	13-3	869
Thalia,					
ex-*Unicorn*	137-1	113-3¾	38-3	13-3	881
Crescent	137-2½	112-10⅜	38-5½	13-3½	888
Romulus	137-2	113-0	38-3	13-3½	879

Notes:

The carronades ordered in Sep 1779 conformed to the Jul 1779 establishment but in Jul 1782 *Flora* carried only 4 x 18pdrs carr on the quarterdeck besides the long guns.

The armament of the upperworks from 1793 is listed in Table 60.

Table 6: *FLORA* CLASS 36-GUN FIFTH RATES
Building Data

Name	Ordered	Builder	Laid down	Launched	Sailed	Fitted at	Fate
Flora	6 Nov 1778	Deptford Dyd	21 Nov 1778	6 May 1780	23 Jun 1780	Deptford	19 Jan 1809 wrecked
Thalia, ex-*Unicorn*	19 Dec 1780	Calhoun, Bursledon	Mar 1781	7 Nov 1782	18 Jan 1783	Portsmouth	15 Aug 1782 renamed; Jul 1814 BU
Crescent	11 Aug 1781	Calhoun, Bursledon	Nov 1781	28 Oct 1784	11 Jan 1785	Portsmouth	6 Dec 1808 wrecked
Romulus	28 Dec 1781	Graves, Deptford	Nov 1782	21 Sep 1785	2 May 1786	Deptford	Jun 1803 harbour service; Nov 1806 BU

The 18pdr ships had their main magazine forward, with a smaller filling room aft, both identifiable by the lantern from the light room. Depth in hold was sufficient to accommodate the forward magazine beneath the fore platform, but aft the rise of the deadwood meant that the magazine was positioned 'hanging' between the lower deck and the hold.

was thinking of numbers of guns but the broadside weight was heavily in favour of the 38: 438lbs to 285lbs for the current 44, and 318lbs for the improved model of 1782, even before carronades were added]; however, the two-decker often could not open her lower deck ports, so was reduced to half the force.

2. With a deep waist and broad gangways, the frigate's crew were as well protected from enemy small arms fire as that of the two-decker.

3. In a single-decker the whole crew was on deck ready to board or oppose boarding.

4. The two-decker was loftier so perforce less weatherly.

5. 'A two-decker can't have so fine a bottom for sailing (which is certainly the first quality of a frigate) as a single-decker; for the two-decker must, like a line-of-battle ship, have a full body, which opposes fleetness, to enable her to carry her lower battery sufficiently above the water.'

The only point Kempenfelt would concede to the 44 was the possible advantage of additional height in action.[15]

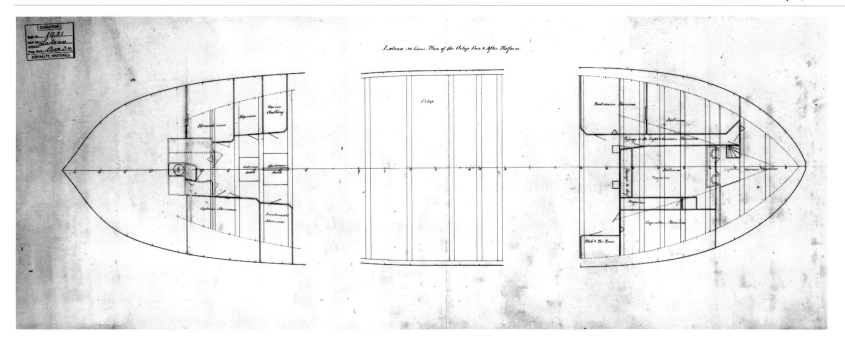

Table 7: *PERSEVERANCE* CLASS 36-GUN FIFTH RATES
Specification

Armament:	Upper deck	Quarterdeck	Forecastle	Guns	Men
Design	26 x 18pdrs	8 x 6pdrs	2 x 6pdrs	36	260
Changed by AO:					
30 Sep 1779 added		4 x 18pdr carr	4 x 18pdr carr		
		12 x ¹/₂pdr swivels			
25 Apr 1780		All 6pdrs replaced with 9pdrs			270
Designed by Sir Edward Hunt					

	Lower deck	Keel	Breadth extreme	Depth in hold	Burthen
	ft-ins	ft-ins	ft-ins	ft-ins	tons
Design	137-0	113-5¹/₂	38-0	13-5	871
As completed					
Perseverance	137-0	113-4¹/₄	38-3	13-5	882
Phoenix	137-1	113-2⁷/₈	38-3³/₄	13-5	884
Inconstant	137-9	114-2	38-3¹/₂	13-5	890
Leda	137-4¹/₂	113-7⁵/₈	38-2¹/₂	13-5	881

Notes:

The carronades ordered in the Jul 1779 establishment were soon found impracticable and in Jul 1782 *Perseverance* carried only 2 x 18pdrs carr on the quarterdeck besides the long guns.

The armament of the upperworks from 1793 is listed in Table 60.

Table 8: *PERSEVERANCE* CLASS 36-GUN FIFTH RATES
Building Data

Name	Ordered	Builder	Laid down	Launched	Sailed	Fitted at	Fate
Perseverance	3 Dec 1779	Randall, Rotherhithe	Aug 1780	10 Apr 1781	3 Jun 1781	Deptford	c1806 hulked; 21 May 1823 sold for BU
Phoenix	20 Jun 1781	Parsons, Bursledon	Aug 1781	15 Jul 1783	Aug 1783	Portsmouth	20 Feb 1816 wrecked
Inconstant	8 Dec 1781	Barnard, Deptford	Dec 1782	28 Oct 1783	22 Mar 1784	Deptford	Nov 1817 BU
Leda	22 Mar 1782	Randall, Rotherhithe	Jan 1783	12 Sep 1783	10 Oct 1783	Deptford	11 Feb 1796 foundered

Latona, 38 guns, design orlop and platforms draught.

The 18pdr classes moved towards standardisation in the layout of platforms, although there were minor differences and improvements. *Latona*'s after platform shows the hanging magazine furthest aft on the centreline; to port are the steward's room, slop room, and Marine clothing store; to starboard, the captain's storeroom and lieutenant's storeroom; access to fish room and spirits store was via hatches on the centreline. The forward platform was larger and more complex: there was a boatswain's store and sail room to port, with a second sail room on the centreline; passages either side of the latter led to the light room and forepeak gunner's store (to port) and magazine (to starboard); on the starboard side was a small pitch and tar room and the carpenter's store.

Nevertheless, the consensus in favour of the 44 was strong enough for nine of them to be started during 1780-81, and an enlarged design with 12pdrs on the upper deck was introduced in 1782. Eight of these were built, but as a belated recognition of the obsolescence of the concept, they spent most of their short active lives as troopships or transports.

After the first 36 and 38 had been laid down in the Dockyards, the follow-on orders went to merchant builders, but in the American war frigates were not built at the breakneck speed of the previous conflict and most were over eighteen months in construction.[16] This meant that the new types did not enter service until mid-1780, but in recompense

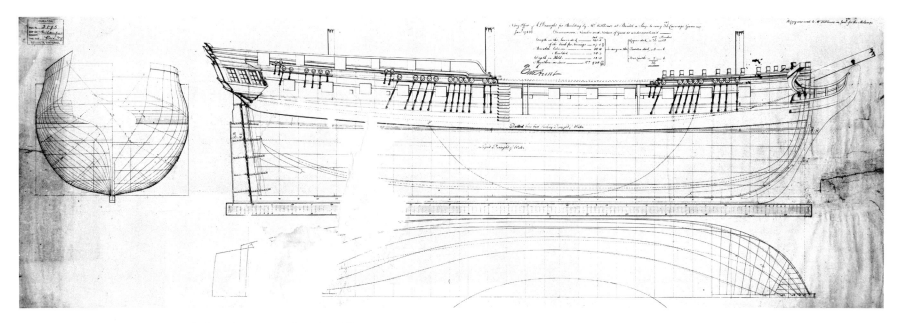

Melampus, 36 guns, design sheer draught, dated January 1783.

This ship was essentially an *Arethusa* reconfigured for two less upper deck ports, the space being allocated to the ends of the battery.

Table 9: *MELAMPUS* CLASS 36-GUN FIFTH RATE
Specification

Armament:	Upper deck	Quarterdeck	Forecastle	Guns	Men
Design	26 x 18pdrs	8 x 9pdrs	2 x 9pdrs	36	270

Designed by Sir Edward Hunt (*Minerva* class 38 with 26 upper deck ports)

	Lower deck	Keel	Breadth extreme	Depth in hold	Burthen
	ft-ins	ft-ins	ft-ins	ft-ins	tons
Design	141-0	117-0 $^3/_8$	38-10	13-11	938$^{72}/_{94}$
As completed					
Melampus	141-2$^1/_4$	117-1	39-0	13-11	947$^{24}/_{94}$

Notes:

The carronades ordered in the Jul 1779 establishment were soon found impracticable, and the ship carried no carronades as completed.

The armament of the upperworks from 1793 is listed in Table 60.

Table 10: *MELAMPUS* CLASS 36-GUN FIFTH RATE
Building Data

Name	Ordered	Builder	Laid down	Launched	Sailed	Fitted at	Fate
Melampus	17 Apr 1782	Hilhouse, Bristol	Dec 1782	8 Jun 1785	8 Sep 1785	Plymouth	Jun 1815 sold to Dutch navy

Notes:

Ordered as a *Minerva* class 38 but altered to a 36 by AO 11 Jan 1783.

Sailed to Plymouth for fitting 13 Jul 1785.

they all enjoyed long active careers. Both classes of 36 seem to have been rather similar in overall performance: they were very robust (as the first 18pdr frigates, the scantlings were very conservative so they were probably somewhat over-built); they were very seaworthy, and able to carry their guns at an unprecedented 7ft freeboard even victualled for six months' Foreign Service. The emphasis was strongly in favour of fighting qualities because they also contrived an unusually spacious 7ft between gunports. However, this could only be achieved on a 137ft length by carrying the battery very close to the ends of the ship, entailing rather full lines; as a result they were not very fast by frigate standards, although they were both manoeuvrable and weatherly.[17] The contemporary ordering pattern suggests no preference for one class over the other but historical judgement favoured Hunt's *Perseverance*.[18]

The 38s possessed most of their advantages but were better performers under sail, although Williams' *Latona* was flawed by her leewardliness and tendency to heavy rolling, shipping water over the waist in high seas. Although they were eclipsed in point of numbers by the 44s, the new 38s were obviously highly thought of. For example, Richard Pearson's reward for his defence of the Baltic convoy against John Paul Jones was not only a knighthood but also command of the *Arethusa*. He was to complain about the weight of her guns, but the Navy Board, feigning their usual surprise, said that to date they had only 'the

Melampus, 36 guns, 1785, contemporary model.

This is one of four excellent models of frigates constructed at the Bristol yard of J M Hilhouse, and assumed to have been commissioned by the builders. Judging by the flying jibboom and double dolphin striker, the rigging at least represents a later stage of the ship's career, but the unusual forecastle barricading – just on the broadside, and not carried around the bow – may indicate an earlier date for the hull fittings. The armament is not quite right for any period: there are two 9pdr chase guns missing from the fore-castle, the only gunport on each side being filled with a carronade; there are also two carronades a side right aft, although one is located in the wrong port (No 5, when it should be No 4). The carronades are not well modelled but they appear to be quite small, and since the ship received six 32pdrs in lieu of six 18pdrs in June 1793 this may give some clue to the dating of the model. *(Bristol Museum and Art Gallery)*

best of characters' of these ships and was adamant that they were built strongly enough to carry them.[19] In fact in response to the representations of Captain Fielding of the *Minerva* they had already increased the armament on the upperworks from 6pdr to 9pdr calibre.

However, they were unable to resist a steady trickle of complaints from the captains of the 38s about the cramped nature of their gun decks. At 141ft there was barely room for fourteen gunports a side (this is evident in the draughts where the aftermost port in particular is jammed right against the quarter gallery) and space between the ports was 6ins less than on the 36s. Eventually the Surveyors decided that thirteen ports 'would answer much better in every respect' and in January 1783 they suggested converting the *Minerva* class 38 in the early stages of construction at Bristol to a 36 by reducing and rearranging the ports.[20] Actually, they did not add any distance between the ports, but by providing space at the ends of the battery reduced weights at the extremities of the ship, and *Melampus*, as the ship was christened, became a fine sailer.[21] In this context it is worth noting that the 38s suffered from heavy pitching, and *Phaeton*'s captain mentions their regular habit of moving the foremost guns aft abreast the main mast in heavy weather to offset this labouring; for the same reason *Thetis*'s captain applied for carronades in place of his foremost upper deck 18pdrs.[22]

Only the the first three 38s and two 36s entered service in time to see much action, but for nearly three years they had no real equals in any enemy navy. Taking the *Flora* as an example, her action with the *Nymphe* on 11 November 1780 was the first to pit an 18pdr frigate against an adversary of similar size – except that the French ship carried only 12pdrs and no carronades, resulting after more than an hour's close engagement in the surrender of the French ship with 55 killed and 81 wounded; *Flora*, by contrast, lost 9 dead and 17 wounded, a foretaste of the disparity that was to become a feature of single-ship engagements in the French Revolutionary War. An even more stubbornly fought action in May 1781 ended in the capture of the Dutch *Castor*, a 12pdr ship with a broadside of 186lbs to her opponent's 333lbs which lost 30 dead and 30 wounded (to the British ship's 17 and 24 respectively).[23]

As with so many aspects of the naval war from 1778 to 1783 there was considerable dissatisfaction with the achievements of cruisers, but Middleton put this down to poor strategy and dispositions and not to inherent faults in the ships. However, a new respect for the French navy grew up amongst many of its adversaries, and for some of the more thoughtful naval officers its success was attributed to a better groundwork of theory, superior officer training, and a more professional attitude to the building, equipment and handling of their ships and fleets.[24] Inevitably, this would lead to a revival of the old inferiority complex about British ship design exorcised by the successes of the Seven Years War, but during the American conflict there was only one example of any interest in building to the lines of a French prize.

In January 1782 the Navy Board proposed building a 36 to the lines of the *Prudente*, in order to utilise a slip that would become free at Sheerness in April. Because of its heavy commitment to refitting and

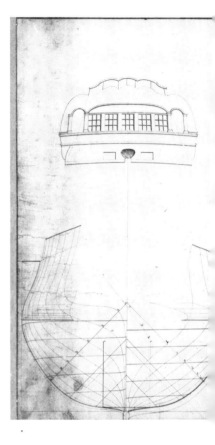

Hebe, 38 guns, ex-French, as fitted sheer & profile draught, dated Plymouth 6 May 1783.

One of the first French 18pdr frigates, *Hebe* was designed by the celebrated naval architect J-N Sané, with a hull form that was to be employed in both France and Britain for half a century. Compared with contemporary British ships, *Hebe* was long and low, and it is noticeable that the main magazine forward has to 'hang' below the level of the fore platform.

repair Sheerness was notoriously slow at new construction, so there was obviously no sense of urgency, but the exact reasons for the choice of prototype are unknown. She was the same size as current 36s, but there are no surviving reports on her sailing qualities to suggest what the supposed advantages of her hull form might be. Her name was certainly before the Navy Board on a regular basis because her armament was always being changed, but the new ship was to carry 18pdrs not 12pdrs like the prototype. Although the ship was registered as the *Cassandra*, when she was cancelled on 21 March 1782 no progress seems to have been made on the design work.[25] The move was prompted by the Admiralty desire to give priority to a 74 at Woolwich at the expense of the 32-gun *Mermaid*; the Navy Board decided that it was of greater benefit to His Majesty's Service to transfer the *Mermaid* to the vacant Sheerness slip than to build the new 36.[26] Clearly, this was not an experiment that anybody felt was essential.

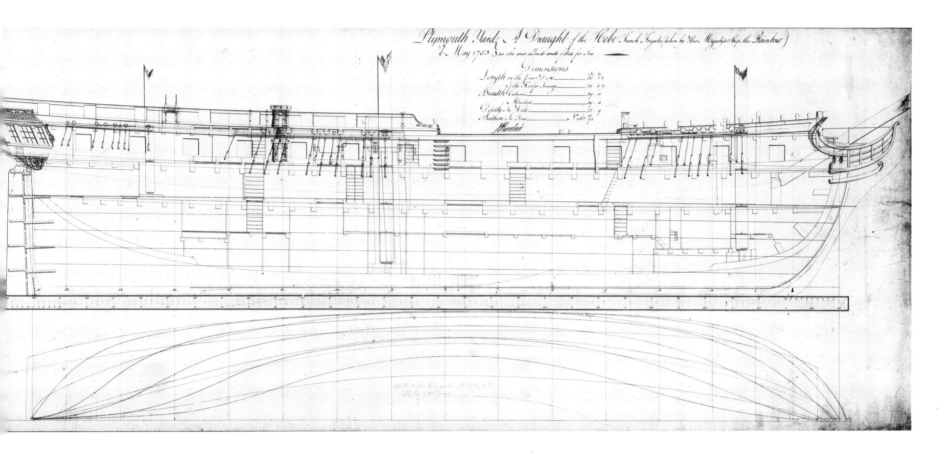

Table 11: CAPTURED SHIPS 1778-1783

Name, rate	Nation-ality	Built	Captured	Dimensions Lower deck ft-ins	Keel ft-ins	Breadth ft-ins	Depth in hold ft-ins	Burthen tons	Armament Upper deck (No x cal)	Quarterdeck (No x cal)	Forecastle (No x cal)	Fate
Artois, 40 ex-*L'Artois*, 40 privateer	Fr	Lorient, 1780	1 Jul 1780	158-8	133-1⁵/₈	40-4	13-6	1152	28 x 18	10 x 9	2 x 9[1]	2 Feb 1786 sold
Hebe, 38 ex-*L'Hébé*, 40	Fr	St Malo, 1782 (Sané design)	9 Sep 1782	151-3¹/₂ 150-1¹/₂	126-1³/₈ 125-4¹/₂	39-11¹/₂ 39-11	12-5¹/₂ 12-9	1071 1062⁵²/₉₄	28 x 18 28 x 18	8 x 9 10 x 8	2 x 9 2 x 8	1798-1805 troopship; 1804 renamed *Blonde*; Jun 1811 BU
Aigle, 38 ex-*L'Aigle*, 40	Fr	St Malo, 1779	14 Sep 1782	150-7 147-5	127-1 122-3	39-1 39-3	18-5 12-2	1032⁶³/₉₄ 1001⁷²/₉₄	28 x 18[2]	8 x 9	2 x 9	18 Jul 1798 wrecked

Notes:

Artois was a large privateer presented to the king by the region of that name; fitted out by Prince Charles, the Count of Artois.

L'Aigle also began life as a privateer but, according to her captors, was in naval service when taken.

Hebe and *Aigle* were remeasured in 1790, giving the second set of figures quoted above (*Aigle* was originally measured abroad and her captors may have exaggerated the dimensions to increase the prize money).

The armament of the upperworks from 1793 is listed in Table 61.

[1] *Artois* received 2 x 68pdr carr for her forecastle by AO 22 Oct 1781; the ship was effectively the trials ship for the 68pdr carronade.

[2] *L'Aigle* was reported to carry 28 x 24pdrs and 16 x 9pdrs (English guns) when captured (see NRS *Barham* I, p210); in Oct 1790 she was established with 26 x 12pdrs and 10 x 6pdrs, but by AO 31 Dec 1792 was rerated 38 and armed as above; 2 x 32pdr carr were added by AO 25 Jan 1793.

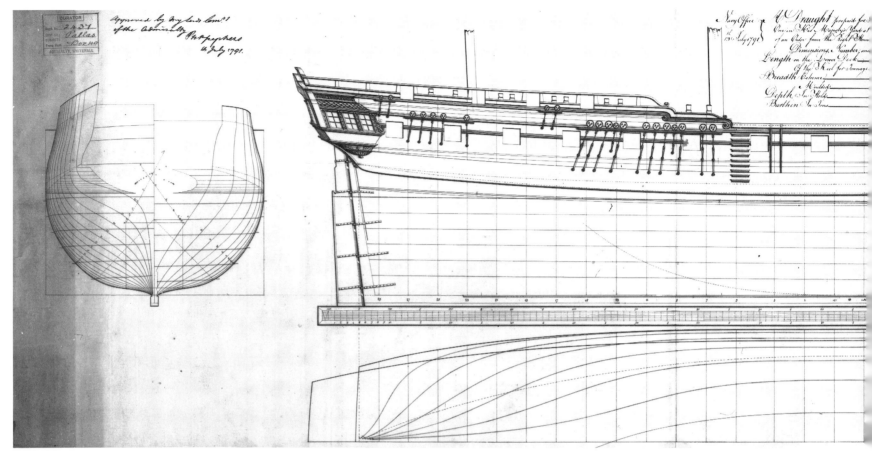

3. A Phase of Gradual Evolution, 1790-1794

Pallas class 32, design sheer draught, dated 13 July 1791.

The first 18pdr 32s were designed to utilise available small scantling timbers in the Royal Dockyards. The class was the first frigate design by Sir John Henslow; a minor stylistic feature of his work was a long, low head characterised by four head timbers, as seen in this class.

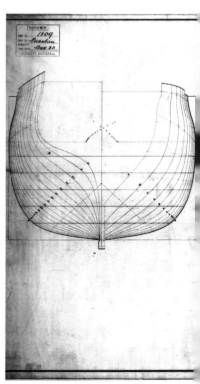

The massive building programmes of the American War left the Royal Navy larger than ever. In 1784 the Comptroller, Middleton, wrote of this 'time of profound peace, when the navy is so complete in the number of ships that that it would be the height of extravagance to build another for at least ten years to come...'.[27] Frigates were not usually built in peacetime in any case, but the peace was not as profound as Middleton forecast, nor the shipbuilding holiday as long. In 1787 the so-called 'Dutch Armament', devised to counter French influence in Holland, saw the first commissionings of many of the late-war 44s but in the role of fast transports; another war scare, over Spanish claims on the Pacific coast of Canada, produced a further Armament in 1790; and an anticipated breach with Russia regarding Turkey a third in 1791.

None of these inspired any frigate-building but a number of existing ships were ordered to be given large repairs in the merchant yards in July 1790[28] and a large frigate building on speculation was purchased

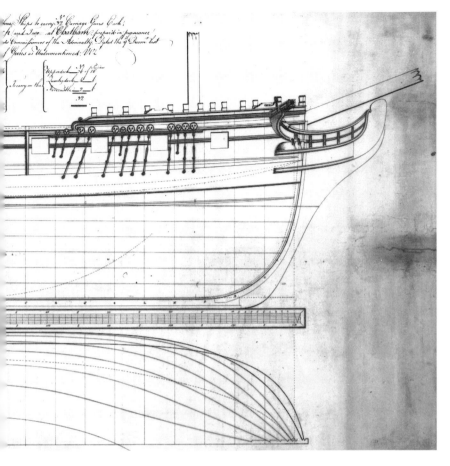

in June of that year at the height of the Spanish emergency. At 1019 tons this vessel was large for the time, and was registered as the *Beaulieu* of 40 guns, a new rating for a single-decker. This was only the second frigate purchased in this way and it may be more than coincidence that the first, the *Heroine*, came from the same firm of Adams at Bucklers Hard.

Middleton, who had been Comptroller since 1778, resigned in 1790 in protest at delay in the administrative overhaul which he had so strongly advocated. From 1783 he had been concerned to put the Dockyards in a state of preparation for the next major war and as such had opposed unnecessary shipbuilding, believing that higher priority should be given to stockpiling timber.[29] After his resignation and in a lull between the Spanish and Russian emergencies, a survey of the Dockyards found that both small slips and 'small timber' were available, so the Navy Board proposed a limited programme to utilise the spare

Beaulieu, 40 guns, 1790, fitting out draught.

This private-venture frigate was purchased on the stocks and fitted out to Royal Navy standards. Internally, she was laid out like a normal 38, but had two more gunports than her establishment of twenty-eight 18pdrs required. The hull form is much fuller than other frigates and closer to that of a merchant ship. This is reflected in the vast tonnage of ballast and water that the ship could stow – nearly twice that of a normal frigate. No sailing quality reports on the ship survive, but it is unlikely that she was much of a sailer, and it may be significant that she was one of the first 18pdr frigates released for service overseas during the French Revolutionary War when the Admiralty was very anxious to keep as many big frigates in the Channel as possible.

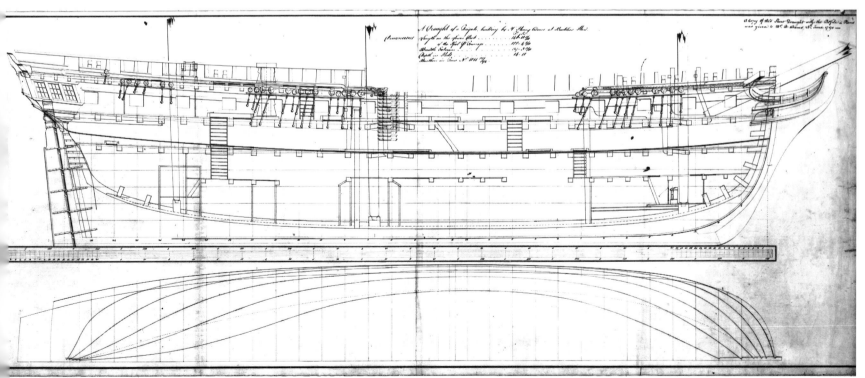

capacity, which the Admiralty approved on 9 December 1790.[30]

Initially two of the three 32s so ordered were allocated to Plymouth and Portsmouth, but as major fleet bases there was greater likelihood of sudden calls on their slipways and in February 1791 the orders were transferred to Chatham and Woolwich respectively. This was Henslow's first frigate design and the draught was not produced until July 1791 – but whether this was the result of inexperience or the usual torpid pace of business in peacetime is impossible to say. The ensuing ships of the *Pallas* class were a typically British attempt at an 18pdr ship on minimum dimensions. Because the only difference between a 32 and a

36 was two gunports a side on the upperworks, the same thirteen upper deck ports had to be incorporated into the shorter length of a smaller ship. However, the gun deck was only 2ft shorter than the preceding 36s, so by reducing the port spacing to the 6½ft of the 38s, the ends of the battery could be kept further from the extremities of the ship – a concern that was to lead to the rapid increase in the overall length of British frigates in the next few years.

The hull form was generally similar to, but marginally sharper than, the earlier 36s with a noticeable hollow in the garboards. In service they were never noted as fast sailers but were excellent sea-boats whose

Table 12: CAPTURED SHIPS 1793-1801

Name, rate	Nationality	Built	Captured	Lower deck ft-ins	Keel ft-ins	Breadth ft-ins	Depth in hold ft-ins	Burthen tons	Quarterdeck (No x cal)	Forecastle (No x cal)	Fate
Armed with 24 x 18pdrs on upper deck											
Tholin, 36 ex-*Thulen*	Du	Zeeland, 1783	8 Jun 1796	143-9½	118-11⅛	39-11¾	13-1½	1011	10 x 6	2 x 6	never cruised; hulk until BU 1811
Armed with 26 x 18pdrs on upper deck											
Modeste, 36	Fr	Toulon, 1786	17 Oct 1793	143-6⅝	118-3	38-8	12-1½	940³⁵/₉₄	8 x 9, *26 x 12 UD, 10 x 6 QD&FC*	2 x 9	1803-5 Trinity House; 1814 BU
San Fiorenzo, 36 ex-*Minerve*, 38	Fr	Toulon, 1782	19 Feb 1794	148-8	124-4⅛	39-6	13-3	1031⁸⁶/₉₄	6 x 6, 6 x 32 carr	2 x 6, 2 x 3 carr	1810 troopship; 1812 hulk; Sep 1837 BU
Saldanha, 40 ex-*Castor*	Du	Rotterdam, 1780	14 Aug 1796	147-3		40-4		1065	10 x 9	4 x 9	1798 hulk; Jan 1806 sold
Immortalité, 36 ex-40	Fr	Lorient, 1795	20 Oct 1798	145-2	123-9¾	39-2	11-5	1010²⁵/₉₄	8 x 9, 4 x 24 carr *24 x 24 UD, 14 x 8 + 4 x 36 carr QD&FC*	2 x 9, 2 x 24 carr	Jul 1806 BU
Princess Charlotte, 36 ex-*Junon*, 38	Fr	Toulon, 1782	18 Jun 1799	148-10	124-9	39-4½	12-10	1028⁷³/₉₄	2 x 9, 12 x 32 carr	2 x 9, 4 x 32 carr	1812 renamed *Andromache*; Jun 1828 BU
Pique, 36 ex-*Pallas*, 38	Fr	St Malo, 1800	6 Feb 1800	146-8	123-1½	39-7½	12-0	1028²⁹/₉₄	2 x 9, 10 x 24 carr	4 x 9, 2 x 24	22 Jul 1819 sold
Desirée, 36 ex-38	Fr	Dunkirk, 1796	8 Jul 1800	147-3	124-2¼	39-2¾	11-9	1016⁵⁰/₉₄	2 x 9, 8 x 32 carr *14 x 8, 2 x 36 carr QD&FC*	2 x 9, 2 x 32 carr	1823 hulk; 28 Aug 1832 sold
Armed with 28 x 18pdrs on upper deck											
Amethyst, 38 ex-*Perle*, 40	Fr	Toulon, 1790	29 Aug 1793	150-4	124-6	39-5	12-10½	1028⁸⁰/₉₄	10 x 6, 6 x 32 carr	2 x 6, 2 x 32 carr	29 Dec 1795 wrecked
Aréthuse, 38 ex-40	Fr	Brest, 1791	29 Aug 1793	152-0	126-10	39-8½	12-4	1064	6 x 6, 4 x 24 carr	4 x 6	1795 renamed *Undaunted*; 27 Aug 1796 wrecked
Impérieuse, 38 ex-40	Fr	Toulon, 1787	11 Oct 1793	148-6	124-10	39-7	12-8	1040³²/₉₄	8 x 9, 6 x 32 carr	2 x 9, 2 x 32 carr	3 Sep 1803 renamed *Unité*; 1836 hulk; Jan 1858 BU
Sybille, 44	Fr	Toulon, 1791	17 Jun 1794	154-3	127-4¾	40-1½	12-4	1090⁹¹/₉₄	12 x 9 *26 x 18 UD, 16 x 8 + 2 x 36 carr QD&FC*	4 x 9	1831 hulk; 7 Aug 1833 sold
Melpomène, 38 ex-40	Fr	Toulon, 1789	10 Aug 1794	148-2	123-8½	39-3	13-6	1014	8 x 9, 6 x 32 carr	2 x 9, 2 x 32 carr	1810 troopship; 14 Dec 1815 sold
Révolutionnaire, 38 ex-44	Fr	Le Havre, 1794	21 Oct 1794	157-2	131-9⅞	40-5½	12-6	1147⁶⁸/₉₄	8 x 9, 6 x 32 carr *12 x 8 + 4 x 36 carr QD&FC*	2 x 9, 2 x 32 carr	Oct 1822 BU
Minerve, 38[1] ex-40	Fr	Toulon, 1794	24 Jun 1795	154-4½	130-0⅛	39-11	13-0	1101⁷⁹/₉₄	8 x 9, 6 x 32 carr 12 x 8 + 2 x 36 carr QD&FC	2 x 9, 2 x 32 carr	3 Jul 1803 captured; recaptured 3 Feb 1810 as *Confiance* but not taken into RN

comparative advantages improved as the weather worsened; they also preserved over 7ft of midships gunport freeboard even when heavily loaded. They were proportionately longer than their predecessors, and some doubts must have been felt about their ability to carry sail because the follow-on *Alcmene* class had 6ins added to the beam, although none of the earlier ships had yet entered service (there is no evidence of any lack of stiffness from sailing reports on the *Pallas* class).

The four ships of the *Alcmene* class were ordered at the same time as six new 38s, the first response of Lord Chatham's Admiralty to the outbreak of war with France. During the peace the limited funding had been concentrated on the battlefleet, so this relatively large programme reflected the immediate need for more frigates. The 38s were a priority because the French navy had built seventeen[31] big frigates since 1782 to which the British could oppose the five American War-built 38s, the purchased *Beaulieu* and two prizes, plus the nine 36s (none of the 32-gun ships of 1790 had yet entered service). Furthermore the size and quality of the French ships were obvious since one of the prototypes of the class, *Hebe*, had been in British hands since 1782. Further big frigates were under construction and eight were supposed to be designed for 24pdrs.[32]

| Name, rate | Nationality | Built | Captured | Dimensions | | | | Burthen | Armament | | Fate |
				Lower deck ft-ins	Keel ft-ins	Breadth ft-ins	Depth in hold ft-ins	tons	Quarterdeck (No x cal)	Forecastle (No x cal)	
Virginie, 38 ex-40	Fr	Brest, 1794	23 Apr 1796	151-3¾	126-3¼	39-10	12-8	1065⁶²/₉₄	8 x 9, 4 x 24 carr *12 x 8 + 4 x 36 carr QD&FC*	2 x 9, 2 x 24 carr	1811 hulk; 11 Jul 1827 sold
Amelia, 38 ex-*Proserpine*, 40	Fr	Brest, 1785	13 Jun 1796	151-4	126-1⅜	39-8 7/8	12-6½	1059³⁵/₉₄	8 x 9, 4 x 24 carr *26 x 18 UD, 14 x 8 + 4 x 36 carr QD&FC*	2 x 9, 2 x 24 carr	Dec 1816 BU
Uranie, 38 ex-*Tartu*, 40	Fr	Lorient, 1788	5 Jan 1797	154-5	128-3½	40-1¾	13-0	1099⁷⁶/₉₄	8 x 9, 4 x 24 carr	2 x 9, 2 x 24 carr	Oct 1807 sold
Fisgard, 38 ex-*Résistance*, 40	Fr	Paimboeuf, 1793	9 Mar 1797	160-6	134-2⅛	40-8½	13-3½	1182¹⁰/₉₄	8 x 9, 6 x 32 carr *² 28 x 18 UD, 14 x 8 + 4 x 36 carr QD&FC*	2 x 9, 2 x 32 carr	11 Aug 1814 sold
Seine, 40	Fr	Le Havre, 1793	30 Jun 1798	156-9	131-4⅛	40-6	12-4½	1145⁸⁷/₉₄	8 x 9	4 x 9	5 Jun 1803 wrecked
Loire, 40	Fr	Nantes, 1795	18 Oct 1798	153-8	128-2⅝	40-2	12-11¾	1100³¹/₉₄	8 x 9, 4 x 24 carr *12 x 8 + 6 x 36 carr QD&FC*	4 x 9, 2 x 24 carr	Apr 1818 BU
Niobe, 38 ex-*Diane*, 40	Fr	Toulon, 1796	24 Aug 1800	155-10	129-6⅞	40-8½	12-7	1142¹⁵/₉₄	2 x 9, 10 x 32 carr	2 x 9, 2 x 32 carr	1814 troopship; Nov 1816 BU
Vengeance, - ex-40	Fr	Paimboeuf, 1793	25 Aug 1800	160-0	147-10	41-9	15-9	1390³	Disarmed in RN *30 x 24 UD, 12 x 12 QD&FC*		never cruised; 1801 hulk until BU 1803
Africaine, 38 ex-40	Fr	Rochefort, 1798	19 Feb 1801	153-10	128-0⅜	39-11	12-6	1085	6 x 9, 8 x 32 carr *18 x 8 QD&FC*	4 x 9, 2 x 32 carr	Sep 1816 BU
Carrère, 38 ex-40	Fr	Venice, 1797	3 Aug 1801	150-10	122-3½	39-5½	12-9	1013	2 x 9, 10 x 32 carr	2 x 9, 2 x 32 carr	never cruised; hulk from 1802 until sold 1 Sep 1814

Notes:

The first and second lines of the armament columns, in roman type, are as first rearmed in British service; the line in *italics* is the original 'as captured' guns, where known. The usual armament of French frigates in 1793 was 28 x 18pdrs, 10 x 8pdrs, plus 4 x 36pdr carr (40-gun ships); 38s had 2 x 18s less.

Later armament changes are listed in Table 61.

[1] Armament assumed: AO of 15 Jun 1798 specifies only 32pdr carr and 9pdr long guns in the wake of the rigging.

[2] The ship was designed for 30 x 24pdrs on the UD (as *Vengeance*), but was armed as above when captured.

[3] The ship was not formally measured in dock and the figures are dubious. She was a sister of *Résistance* and cannot have varied much; some sources give a tonnage figure of 1180 which seems more likely. See J Boudriot, 'L'Egyptienne', *Neptunia* 175 (1989).

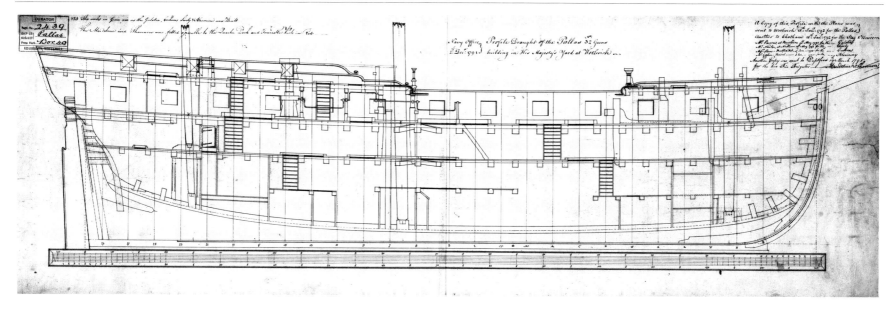

Pallas class 32, design profile draught, dated 2 December 1791.

Unlike the bigger ships, the 18pdr 32s followed the internal layout of their 12pdr classmates, with a small hanging magazine forward, and the main magazine aft. This profile was used for the *Pallas* class and their *Alcmene* class half-sisters, as well as the fir-built *Shannon* and *Maidstone* (which were armed with 12pdrs). The *Alcmene*s had the aftermost quarterdeck ports enlarged for carronades (and a sill cut for one on the forecastle) – marked in green on the original; the fir ships had square-hanced solid quarterdeck barricades, indicated in red on the draught.

Table 13: *BEAULIEU* CLASS 40-GUN FIFTH RATE
Specification

Armament:	Upper deck	Quarterdeck	Forecastle	Guns	Men
Design	28 x 18pdrs	8 x 9pdrs	4 x 9pdrs	40	280
Changes by AO:					
1793 added		6 x 18pdr carr	2 x 32pdr carr		274
Designed by builder					

	Lower deck	Keel	Breadth extreme	Depth in hold	Burthen
	ft-ins	ft-ins	ft-ins	ft-ins	tons
As completed	147-3	122-10⅝	39-6	15-2⅝	1020

Notes:

Building on speculation and purchased during the 'Spanish Armament' of 1790.
Armament of the upperworks after 1793 is listed in Table 60.

The new 38s, to become the *Artois* class, were very similar in proportions to the *Pallas* class and might be regarded as scaled-up versions. They were 5ft longer than the 38s of 1778 and by preserving the port spacing of 6½ft the extra length was devoted to the ends of the ship – particularly forward. Designed to allow sharper lines and reduce pitching, the process of extending the space beyond the gun battery had been gathering pace since the decision to reduce the *Melampus* to a 36 in 1782. It was not entirely successful in this class, since heavy and quick pitching was their only real vice,[33] nor were they an improvement speed-wise over their predecessors (12kts sailing large is the best quoted for any of them). However, the *Artois* class espoused the traditional British cruising ship virtues of being weatherly, manoeuvrable and sea-kindly; stored for Channel Service they carried their ports about 8ft from the water and exceeded 7ft deep laden, about a foot more than their French counterparts and allowing the lee guns to be fought in any weather – an important advantage when employing the aggressive attack-from-windward tactics favoured by the Royal Navy.

In the early 1790s it had become something of a commonplace among those interested in naval matters that the sailing qualities of British ships were compromised by their being proportionately too short. An influential exponent of this view was the Society for the Improvement of Naval Architecture, set up in 1791, which repeated the assertion in one of the first publications under its auspices, Sir John Borlase Warren's *View of the Naval Force of Great Britain*.[34] A vice-president of the society was Sir Charles Middleton, who was to bring

Table 14: *BEAULIEU* CLASS 40-GUN FIFTH RATE
Building Data

Name	Purchased	Builder	Laid down	Launched	Sailed	Fitted at	Fate
Beaulieu	Jun 1790[1]	Adams, Bucklers Hard		4 May 1791	31 May 1791[2]	Portsmouth	1809 BU

Notes:

[1] Registered and established 16 Jun 1790.

[2] Fitted for Ordinary.

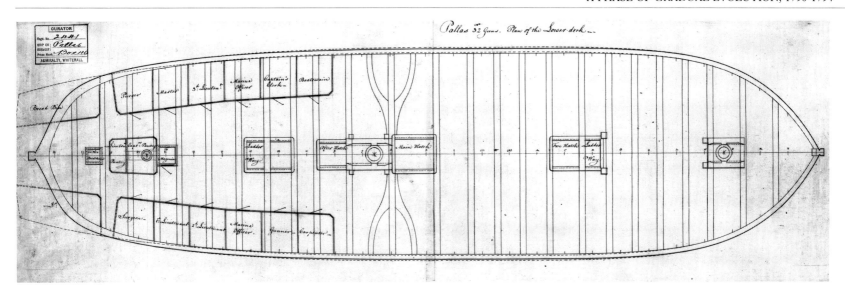

Pallas **class 32, design lower deck draught.**

The layout of cabins on the lower deck was virtually standardised for all
frigate classes in the 1790s. On the port side, from aft forward, they were
occupied by: purser, master, third lieutenant, Marine officer, captain's clerk,
and boatswain. On the starboard side they accommodated: the surgeon, first
lieutenant, second lieutenant, Marine officer, gunner, and carpenter. The last
two on each side were not members of the wardroom. Aft, around the
mizzen mast, were the captain's and lieutenant's pantries.

Pallas **class 32, design orlop and platforms draught.**

Compared with larger frigates, the layout of storerooms on the platforms
had to be somewhat rearranged to account for the reversal of the magazine
spaces. On the after platforms, the spaces were in the same relative positions
but a little smaller; on the fore platform, there were a number of differences,
with the forepeak divided into boatswain's (port) and gunner's stores, a large
sail room to port and a carpenter's store to starboard; there were also
cupboard-like block (port) and pitch rooms.

twelve years' experience as Comptroller of the Navy Board to his role
of Naval Lord when he joined the Admiralty in May 1794. It is no
coincidence that the matter of length soon became an issue, with new
and longer 74s being ordered later in the year.[35]

However, Middleton also believed that the French battlefleet could
be contained to the point where a serious *guerre de course* would be the
only strategy open to France. In this circumstance cruising ships would
be the key to the current war and numbers would become the paramount
requirement.[36] The obvious compromise between power and expense
was the 36-gun ship and six new vessels were ordered within two weeks
of Middleton joining the Admiralty. The current obsession with length
is to be seen in the order to add about five feet to Hunt's *Inconstant*
design, the only existing prototype. The addition, in fact, only brought
the ships to Henslow's preferred length:breadth ratio of 3.75, which was
not as high as the ensuing 74s were to be. At the same time the junior
Surveyor, William Rule, was allowed to build his first frigate design to
a similar overall specification.

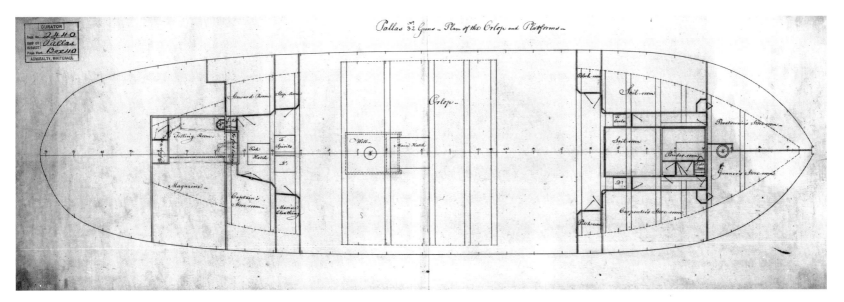

Table 15: *PALLAS* CLASS 32-GUN FIFTH RATES
Specification

Armament:	Upper deck	Quarterdeck	Forecastle	Guns	Men
Design	26 x 18pdrs	4 x 6pdrs	2 x 6pdrs	32	257
Changes by AO:					
26&31 Jul 1794 added (*Stag*):		4 x 32pdr carr	2 x 32pdr carr		
26 Aug 1794 added (*Unicorn*):		4 x 32pdr carr	2 x 32pdr carr		
20 June 1796					254
Designed by Sir John Henslow					

	Lower deck	Keel	Breadth extreme	Depth in hold	Burthen
	ft-ins	ft-ins	ft-ins	ft-ins	tons
Design	135-0	112-8¼	36-0	12-6	776
As completed					
Pallas	135-0½	112-8½	36-0¼	12-6	778
Stag	135-11¼	113-6⅛	36-2¾	12-5¾	792
Unicorn	135-8¾	113-3⅝	36-2¾	12-5¾	791

Notes:

The class completed before the revised carronade establishment was promulgated and as completed the ships carried varied quarterdeck and forecastle armament: see Table 60.

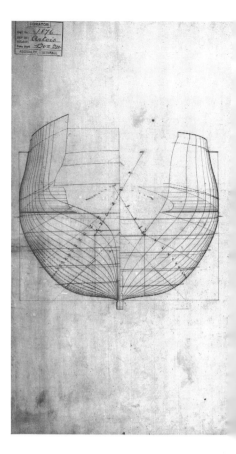

Artois class 38, design sheer draught, dated 22 February 1793.

The first war-inspired programme of big frigates comprised the six ships of the *Artois* class (two fir-built and one more oak-built ships were added later). The annotations note that the ships were built to the ticked lines which indicate slightly fuller frames in the after body and a raised gunwale to make the gangways flush; also that the fore masts of *Jason* and *Diana* were moved forward 6½ins by order of 3 October 1797, and that *Jason* had 3ins extra false keel added by order of 31 July 1798.

Artois class 38, 1794, contemporary model.

There are three fine models of ships of this class in the National Maritime Museum. This particular example was built for the designer, Sir John Henslow, and remained in his family until presented to the museum. Although it has elaborate carved work at bow and stern, it is otherwise not much more detailed than the design draught, and so presumably the model was built before the ship was completed.

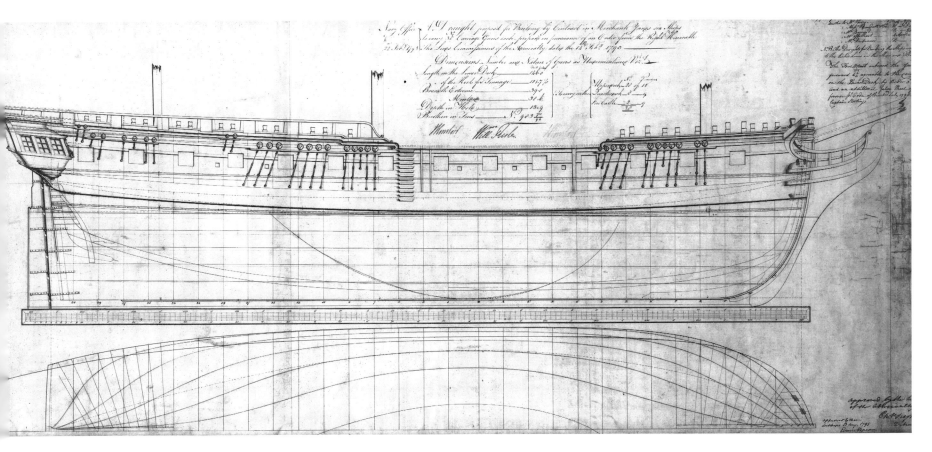

In the four ships ordered as the *Phoebe* class Henslow chose to increase the 7ft gunport spacing of the *Inconstant*s, resulting in the extreme gunports being very near the ends of the ship. Not surprisingly, the class was found to pitch heavily and an attempt was made to remedy this with the *Fortunee*, a late addition to the class, in which the foremost port was moved aft about a foot. Otherwise, they were slightly faster than Henslow's previous ships, but not very stiff, and even *Fortunee* continued to labour, particularly in a head sea.

Because a 'stretched *Inconstant*' was regarded as the safer bet, only two of the six new 36s were built to the design of the untried Rule. The *Amazon* and *Emerald* revealed an opposite view of gunport spacing, reducing the interval to about 6¾ft, shortening the overall length of the battery from 128ft in the *Phoebe*s to 120ft. This helped to make the class more sea-kindly than Henslow's design but they were not as fast in optimum conditions; both classes carried their guns well and were handy in staying and wearing.

Middleton had injected some professionalism into the laissez-faire proceedings of Lord Chatham's Board but by the autumn of 1794, with a rising tide of criticism levelled at delay and confusion in the Dockyards, its days were clearly numbered. An increased level of activity required more energy and organisation and in December Lord Spencer was appointed First Lord. Middleton stayed on, expecting to retain the degree of influence he had exerted over Chatham, but although the new administration revealed a remarkable openness to innovation, Spencer had his own coterie of advisers; this inner cabinet did not include Middleton and increasing resentment at being marginalised drove him from office before the end of 1795. Nevertheless, in technical matters the next few years were to be among the most remarkable in the history of the Royal Navy.

Traditionally Britain makes a poor start in her wars but this was not the case in the struggle with Revolutionary France. Since the First Coalition included virtually all the naval powers – the only major

Table 16: *PALLAS* CLASS 32-GUN FIFTH RATES
Building Data

Name	Ordered	Builder	Laid down	Launched	Sailed	Fitted at	Fate
Pallas	9 Dec 1790	Woolwich Dyd	May 1792	19 Dec 1793	5 Mar 1794	Woolwich	4 Apr 1798 wrecked
Stag	9 Dec 1790	Chatham Dyd	Mar 1792	28 Jun 1794	16 Aug 1794	Chatham	6 Sep 1800 wrecked
Unicorn	9 Dec 1790	Deptford Dyd	Mar 1792	12 Jul 1794	5 Oct 1794	Chatham	Mar 1815 BU at Deptford

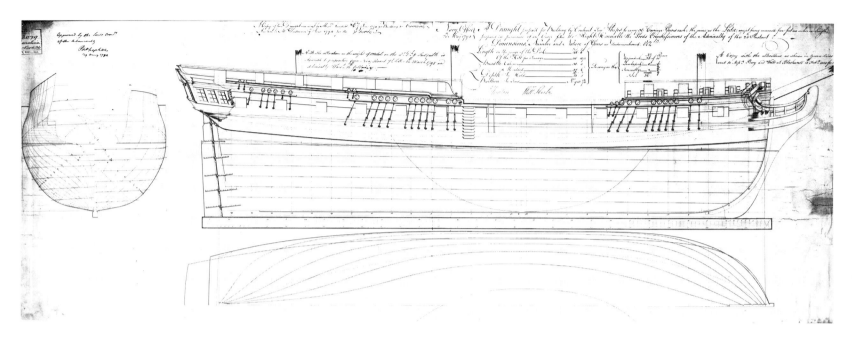

Table 17: *ALCMENE* CLASS 32-GUN FIFTH RATES
Specification

Armament:	Upper deck	Quarterdeck	Forecastle	Guns	Men
Design	26 x 18pdrs	4 x 6pdrs	2 x 6pdrs	32	257
Changes by AO:					
19 Nov 1794 added		4 x 24pdr carr	2 x 24pdr carr		241
20 Jun 1796					254

Designed by Sir John Henslow (Improved *Pallas* class with 6ins more beam)

	Lower deck	Keel	Breadth extreme	Depth in hold	Burthen
	ft-ins	*ft-ins*	*ft-ins*	*ft-ins*	*tons*
Design	135-0	112-4¼	36-6	12-6	796
As completed					
Galatea	135-3	112-5¼	36-9	12-6	808
Cerberus	135-1	112-2³/₈	36-9	12-6	806
Lively	135-3	112-5¼	38-8½	12-6	806
Alcmene	135-3	112-8	36-7½	12-6	803

Notes:

Maidstone and *Shannon* were fir-built versions of this class; they were completed with 12pdr upper deck guns and are detailed in the companion volume in this series, *The First Frigates*. The carronade armament quoted above is the formal establishment for 18pdr 32s. For changes to armament carried on the upperworks see Table 60.

Table 18: *ALCMENE* CLASS 32-GUN FIFTH RATES
Building Data

Name	Ordered	Builder	Laid down	Launched	Sailed	Fitted at	Fate
Galatea	14 Feb 1794	Parsons, Bursledon	Apr 1793	17 May 1794	12 Aug 1794[1]	Portsmouth	May 1809 BU
Cerberus	14 Feb 1794	Adams, Bucklers Hard	Apr 1793	25 Sep 1794	20 Feb 1795	Portsmouth	29 Sep 1814 sold
Lively	14 Feb 1794	Nowlan, Northam	Apr 1793	23 Oct 1794	2 Jan 1795	Portsmouth	12 Apr 1798 wrecked
Alcmene	14 Feb 1794	Graham, Harwich	Apr 1793	8 Nov 1794	12 Apr 1795[2]	Chatham	29 Apr 1809 wrecked

Notes: [1] Docked Portsmouth 23 May 1794.   [2] Coppered 13 Dec 1794 - 5 Jan 1795.

Phoebe class 36, design sheer draught, dated 28 May 1794.

This class was a 'stretched' *Inconstant*, but with the gunports redistributed evenly along the new length. The annotations note the upgrading of secondary armament from 6pdrs to 9pdrs by Navy Board suggestion of 14 March 1795. The alterations, sent on 13 February 1800, are for the *Fortunee* and consist of a redesigned head to move No 1 gunport aft and work in a bridle port; the forecastle is berthed up, and the quarterdeck barricading brought forward, with an extra port, to a square hance.

exceptions were the Baltic states – the allies in theory could count on overwhelming superiority at sea. The occupation of Toulon in 1793 eroded the numbers of the serviceable French warships for some time, even if the chance to reduce the numbers permanently was not grasped as firmly as it might have been. Furthermore, the first major clash between the opposing battlefleets at the Glorious First of June in 1794 revealed that the quality of the French navy had been seriously degraded by the Revolution, which had abolished the special cadre of sea gunners and purged the officer corps of most of its men of experience and talent.

However, 1794 was to see some ominous developments, most worrying being the occupation of the Netherlands and the establishment of a French puppet state called the Batavian Republic. Not for the first (or the last) time the Royal Navy had to evacuate a British army[37] from the Continent and the country's efforts were henceforth concentrated on

Table 19: *ARTOIS* CLASS 38-GUN FIFTH RATES
Specification

Armament:	Upper deck	Quarterdeck	Forecastle	Guns	Men
Design	28 x 18pdrs	8 x 9pdrs	2 x 9pdrs	38	270
Changes by AO:					
19 Nov 1794 added		6 x 32pdr carr	2 x 32pdr carr		
20 Jun 1796					284
Designed by Sir John Henslow					

	Lower deck	Keel	Breadth extreme	Depth in hold	Burthen
	ft-ins	ft-ins	ft-ins	ft-ins	tons
Design	146-0	121-7 $^{1}/_{8}$	39-0	13-9	984
Design (fir ships)	146-0	121-4$^{3}/_{4}$	39-2	13-9	991
As completed					
Artois	146-3	121-9$^{3}/_{4}$	39-2$^{1}/_{2}$	13-9	996
Diana	146-3	121-8$^{1}/_{2}$	39-3$^{1}/_{2}$	13-9	998
Diamond	146-0	121-6	39-3	13-9	996
Apollo	146-3	121-10	39-2	13-9	994
Jason	146-3	121-9	39-3	13-9	998
Seahorse	146-4	121-10	39-3	13-9$^{1}/_{2}$	998
Clyde [fir]	146-0	122-0$^{3}/_{4}$	39-3$^{1}/_{2}$	13-9	1002
Tamer [fir]	146-0	121-10$^{1}/_{2}$	39-3	13-9	999
Ethalion	146-1	121-7	39-2	13-9	992
Clyde [fir]					

Notes:

The fir ships had modifications to the details of scantlings but a square tuck stern was the only major external difference. *Tamer* refers to the river Tamar, but was usually spelt with an 'e' in Admiralty documents.

The carronade armament quoted above is the formal establishment for 38s; individual ships were equipped according to their captain's wishes. For changes to the armament of the upperworks see Table 60.

Table 21: *PHOEBE* CLASS 36-GUN FIFTH RATES
Specification

Armament:	Upper deck	Quarterdeck	Forecastle	Guns	Men
Design	26 x 18pdrs	8 x 6pdrs	2 x 6pdrs	36	
Changes by AO:					
16 Mar 1795		6pdrs changed to 9pdrs			
16 Mar 1795 added		6 x 32pdr carr	2 x 32pdr carr		264
Designed by Sir John Henslow (lengthened version of Hunt's *Inconstant*)					

	Lower deck	Keel	Breadth extreme	Depth in hold	Burthen
	ft-ins	ft-ins	ft-ins	ft-ins	tons
Design	142-6	118-10$^{1}/_{2}$	38-0	13-5	913
As completed					
Dryad	142-8	119-0	38-2$^{1}/_{2}$	13-5	924
Caroline	142-6	118-9$^{1}/_{2}$	38-3	13-5$^{1}/_{2}$	924
Doris	142-6	118-11	38-1	13-5	915
Phoebe	142-9	119-0	38-3	13-5$^{1}/_{2}$	926
Fortunee	142-8	119-0	38-1$^{1}/_{2}$	13-5	921

Notes:

The 6pdr secondary armament was copied from the original *Inconstant* draught (which was also changed to 9pdrs before the ships entered service).

The carronade armament quoted above is as first established by AO of that date for *Caroline*.

For later changes to the armament of the upperworks see Table 60.

Table 20: *ARTOIS* CLASS 38-GUN FIFTH RATES
Building Data

Name	Ordered	Builder	Laid down	Launched	Sailed	Fitted at	Fate
Artois	14 Feb 1793	Wells, Deptford	Mar 1793	3 Jan 1794	30 Mar 1794	Deptford	31 Jul 1797 wrecked
Diana	14 Feb 1793	Randall, Rotherhithe	Mar 1793	3 Mar 1794	6 Jun 1794	Deptford	7 Mar 1815 sold to Dutch
Diamond	14 Feb 1793	Barnard, Deptford	Apr 1793	17 Mar 1794	9 Jun 1794	Deptford	Jun 1812 BU
Apollo	14 Feb 1793	Perry, Blackwall	Mar 1793	18 Mar 1794	23 Sep 1794	Woolwich	7 Jan 1799 wrecked
Jason	14 Feb 1793	Dudman, Deptford	Apr 1793	3 Apr 1794	25 Jul 1794	Deptford	13 Aug 1798 wrecked
Seahorse	14 Feb 1793	Stalkartt, Rotherhithe	Mar 1793	11 Jun 1794	16 Sep 1794	Deptford	Jul 1819 BU
Clyde [fir]	4 Feb 1795	Chatham Dyd	Jun 1795	26 Mar 1796	21 Jun 1796	Chatham	19 Feb 1805 BU began
Tamer [fir]	4 Feb 1795	Chatham Dyd	Jun 1795	26 Mar 1796	21 Jun 1796	Chatham	Jan 1810 BU
Ethalion	30 Apr 1795	Graham, Harwich	Oct 1795	14 Mar 1797	11 Jul 1797	Chatham	19 Dec 1799 wrecked
Clyde [fir]	19 Oct 1804	Woolwich Dyd	Jun 1805	20 Feb 1806	9 Mar 1806	Woolwich	1810 laid up; 1814 sold

Notes:

The first *Clyde* was broken up, but the Navy Board felt that there were sufficient serviceable remains to warrant building another ship using the knees, floor timbers, iron stanchions, masts, yards, fittings and furniture.

Table 22: *PHOEBE* CLASS 36-GUN FIFTH RATES
Building Data

Name	Ordered	Builder	Laid down	Launched	Sailed	Fitted at	Fate
Dryad	24 May 1794	Barnard, Deptford	Jun 1794	4 Jun 1795	15 Aug 1795[1]	Woolwich	1832 hulked; Feb 1860 BU
Caroline	24 May 1794	Randall, Rotherhithe	Jun 1794	17 Jun 1795	25 Sep 1795[2]	Deptford	1813 hulked; Sep 1815 BU
Doris	24 May 1794	Cleveley, Gravesend	Jun 1794	31 Aug 1795	26 Nov 1795[3]	Woolwich	21 Jan 1801 wrecked
Phoebe	24 May 1794	Dudman, Deptford	Jun 1794	24 Sep 1795	23 Dec 1795	Deptford	1826 hulked; 27 May 1841 sold for BU
Fortunee	28 Jan 1800	Perry, Blackwall	Apr 1800	17 Nov 1800	14 Jan 1801	Woolwich	29 Jan 1818 sold for BU

Notes:

[1] Coppered at Deptford 5-16 Jun 1795.

[2] Coppered by builder 18 Jun - 17 Jul 1795.

[3] Coppered by builder 1-17 Sep 1795.

sea power and subsidies – the latter to keep allied armies in the field. The new strategic situation was symbolised by the famous incident of the surrender of the icebound Dutch fleet to a squadron of French hussars! The Dutch navy was not strong,[38] but to the allies the effect of its loss was doubled because it was now under French control, and keeping an eye on it was to become an additional British commitment. On 19 January 1795 an order went out to seize Dutch ships and in February Vice-Admiral Duncan was sent off the Texel with a squadron of observation.

Less than a week after the decision to move against the Dutch the

Admiralty ordered six frigates to be built of fir in merchant yards 'as expeditiously as possible'. These vessels were almost certainly proposed with the North Sea station in mind, and shortly after commissioning four of them were serving with Duncan in January 1797.[39] Numbers of cruisers was also becoming a more general issue, since the French were suspected of making strenuous efforts to increase their frigate force: one of Middleton's correspondents claimed in June 1794 that the French had built one frigate at Le Havre in six weeks.[40] Softwood ships were an obvious riposte, but the new vessels were not built as quickly as the fir frigates of 1757[41] – which were much smaller ships – but the Navy Board

Table 23: *AMAZON* CLASS 36-GUN FIFTH RATES
Specification

Armament:	Upper deck	Quarterdeck	Forecastle	Guns	Men
Design	26 x 18pdrs	8 x 9pdrs	2 x 9pdrs	36	
Changes by AO:					
16 Mar 1795 added;		6 x 32pdr carr	2 x 32pdr carr		264
8 Sep 1795 changed (fir ships)			2 x 12pdrs replace 2 x 9pdrs		
Designed by Sir William Rule					

	Lower deck	Keel	Breadth extreme	Depth in hold	Burthen
	ft-ins	ft-ins	ft-ins	ft-ins	tons
Design	143-0	119-6	38-2	13-6	926
As completed					
Amazon	143-2½	119-5½	38-4	13-6	934
Emerald	143-2½	119-5½	38-4	13-6	934
Trent [fir]	143-0	119-6	38-2	13-6	926
Glenmore ex-*Tweed* [fir]	143-0	119-6	38-2	13-6	926

Notes:

Later armament changes are listed in Table 60.

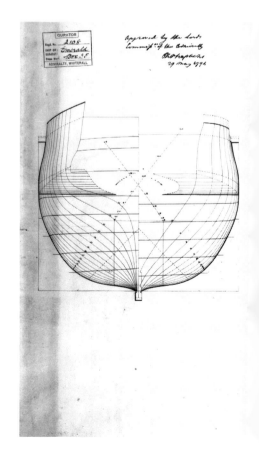

Amazon class 36, design sheer draught, dated 28 May 1794.

Alongside the derivative *Phoebe* class, William Rule was allowed to design an *ab initio* 36-gun class of similar overall dimensions, which became the *Amazon* class. The battery of these ships was more compact, leaving more space between the endmost guns and the stem and stern.

Table 24: *AMAZON* CLASS 36-GUN FIFTH RATES
Building Data

Name	Ordered	Builder	Laid down	Launched	Sailed	Fitted at	Fate
Amazon	24 May 1794	Wells, Rotherhithe	Jun 1794	4 Jul 1795	25 Sep 1795	Deptford[1]	14 Jan 1797 wrecked
Emerald	24 May 1794	Pitcher, Northfleet	Jun 1794	31 Jul 1795	12 Oct 1795	Woolwich[2]	1822 hulked; Jan 1836 BU
Trent [fir]	24 Jan 1795	Woolwich Dyd	Mar 1795	24 Feb 1796	26 May 1796	Woolwich	1803 hospital ship; 1818 hulked; Feb 1822 BU
Glenmore, ex-*Tweed*[3] [fir]	24 Jan 1795	Woolwich Dyd	Mar 1795	24 Mar 1976	3 Jun 1796	Woolwich	1805 hulked; 3 Nov 1814 sold

Notes:

[1] Coppered by builder; to Deptford 3 Sep 1795.

[2] Coppered by builder, 1-17 Aug 1795.

[3] Name changed by AO 30 Oct 1795; celebrates the Duke of Gordon's forest from where the timber was obtained.

experienced the same difficulties getting reasonable tenders from the merchant builders, who were suspicious of the material. As a result they had to be built in the Dockyards, despite a strong Admiralty preference for confining the Dockyards to essential repairs and refitting.

The new programme consisted of pairs of ships built to existing designs: the 32s were to the *Alcmene* draught, the 36s to Hunt's *Amazon*, and the 38s were of the *Artois* class. Although nominally fir-built, the scantlings for these ships included oak for important structural members like stem and sternposts, apron, deadwood and the planking of the square tuck stern, the one obvious external sign of a softwood ship.

Considerable use was made of iron for knees, stanchions and fastenings, although oak was employed for riders and breasthooks.[42] The dimensions of the main framed timbers were not increased as one would expect for strength – although the Navy Board substituted 12pdrs for the intended 18pdrs on the 32s – and the overall result was to produce a hull that was substantially lighter than an oak-built sister (the launching draught of water was usually at least 1ft less). The reduced draught was obviously valuable amongst the shoals and sandbars of the Dutch coast, and the correspondingly greater gunport freeboard would prove useful in a sea where bad weather was the rule rather than the exception.[43]

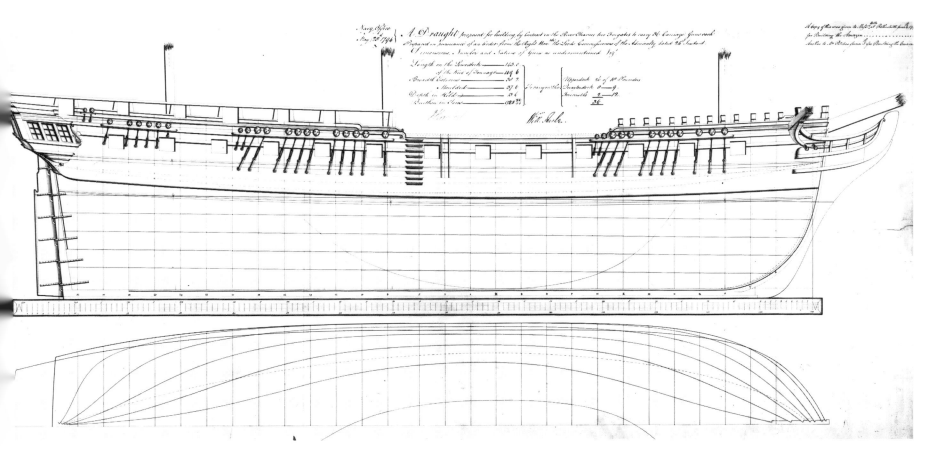

These are the positive aspects of the Admiralty's thinking, but the relative weakness of the Dutch navy and the smallness of its ships made the North Sea squadron a poor relation, always receiving second class ships; undoubtedly the fir frigates were regarded similarly, as quick interim solutions.

In the event they were probably required to serve longer than anticipated and accumulated experience threw up some advantages.[44] Once off the North Sea station they tended to be ballasted to the same waterline as their hardwood sisters by shipping great quantities of iron ballast, which made them very stiff; it could also make them uneasy seaboats but their ability to carry sail meant that they often turned in better performances in terms of sheer speed – *Glenmore* recorded a knot more than any of her sisters and *Clyde* was so highly regarded that when she was worn out a replacement was built utilising her 'serviceable remains'.[45]

Fir-built *Amazon* class 36, design sheer draught, dated 2 February 1795.

The six-ship softwood building programme of 1795 comprised three groups of two ships modified from existing 32-, 36- and 38-gun designs. The 36s were based on Rule's *Amazon,* and as can be observed, the visible changes were minimal: there is a square tuck stern evident in the body plan, and an austerity billet head. There are pencil alterations making the after body far fuller below, but no indication that these changes were adopted; the only alteration noted is the addition of 5in to the false keel of *Glenmore.*

San Fiorenzo, ex-French *Minerve,* 34 guns, as fitted sheer & profile draught, taken off at Chatham and approved by the Admiralty, 13 August 1795.

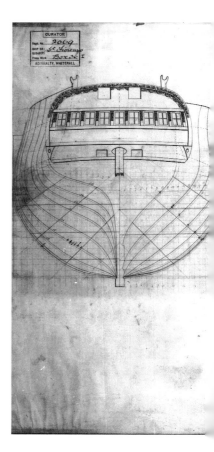

Although this is an as fitted draught, the changes to the original French arrangements are minimal, the only obvious features being the extra, larger, ports cut on the quarterdeck and forecastle to take the 32pdr carronades (six and two respectively) added to the ship's 34 long guns. French features include the original arrangement of capstans, beakhead bulkhead, wheel abaft the mizzen, the complete decorative scheme, and the layout of platforms. Below decks note the absence of an orlop and the small separate magazine and filling room aft (identified by two lanterns from an intervening light room). This was a 'first generation' 18pdr frigate designed by J M B Coulomb towards the end of a distinguished career; it was neither as large nor as sharp-lined as some later ships and was also more capacious, which may have been the factors that made this ship attractive to an Admiralty seeking a potential prototype. The approval date, which is the same for the *Impérieuse* and *Melpomène* draughts, marks the decision to copy the lines of these ships.

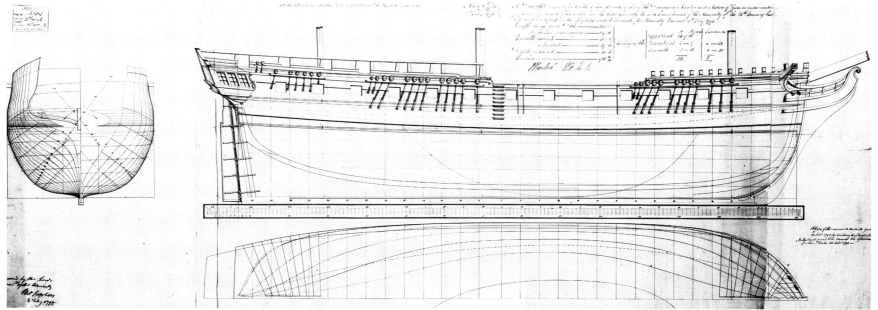

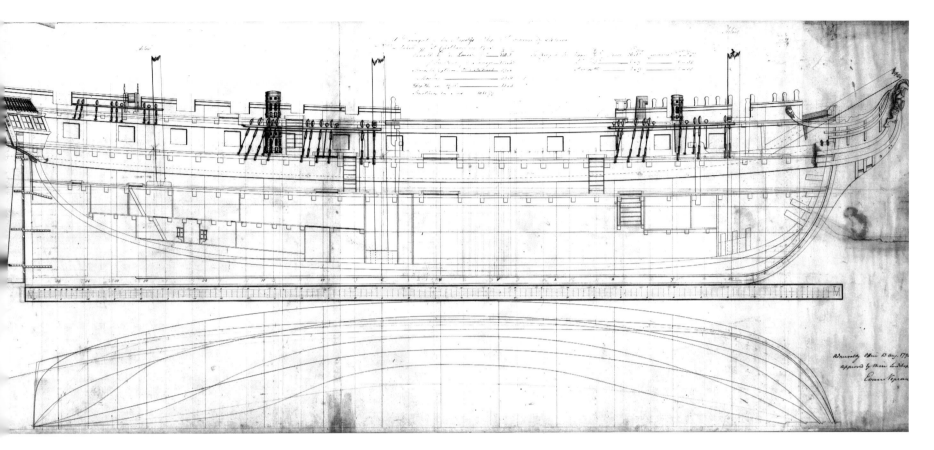

4. The 'French Programme', 1795

By the end of 1794 the idea that the war would be short was losing ground and the Admiralty began to make longer term plans. On 7 January 1795 the Navy Board was ordered to approach the merchant builders to find out how many 74s and frigates could be built quickly. During the latter stages of the American War when more ships were wanted than there was capacity available, the Navy Board usually responded to approaches from shipbuilders rather than Admiralty orders; the Admiralty would approve or refuse the proposed contract, but did not initiate the process, the Navy Board following a general direction on requirements.[46] A similar system began to take shape in 1795. Based on the Navy Board's discussions with the builders, some sixteen new frigates seemed possible at first, but this was reduced to eleven after more detailed discussions.[47] However, in February 1795 the whole of this programme foundered on the prices being demanded by

Table 25: *SIRIUS* CLASS 36-GUN FIFTH RATE
Specification

Armament:	Upper deck	Quarterdeck	Forecastle	Guns	Men
Design	26 x 18pdrs	6 x 9pdrs	2 x 9pdrs	36	264
Changes by AO:					
7 Nov 1797					274[1]

'Similar to *San Fiorenzo*' (French *Minerve* captured 19 Feb 1794)

	Lower deck ft-ins	Keel ft-ins	Breadth extreme ft-ins	Depth in hold ft-ins	Burthen tons
Design	148-10	124-0³⁄₈	39-7	13-3	1034
As completed					
Sirius[2]	148-10	124-0¹⁄₈	39-10	13-3	1047

Notes:

[1] The Navy Board allowed 10 extra men because the ship carried the masts and spars of a 38. Note that the ship carried only 34 guns, and was rated as such in some lists.

[2] Although the modern spelling is '*Sirius*', official contemporary sources quote the name as *Syrius*'. Armament changes are listed in Table 60.

Table 26: *SIRIUS* CLASS 36-GUN FIFTH RATE
Building Data

Name	Ordered	Builder	Laid down	Launched	Sailed	Fitted at	Fate
Sirius	30 Apr 1795	Dudman, Deptford	Sep 1795	12 Apr 1797	24 Jun 1797	Deptford	23 Aug 1810 destroyed to avoid capture, Mauritius

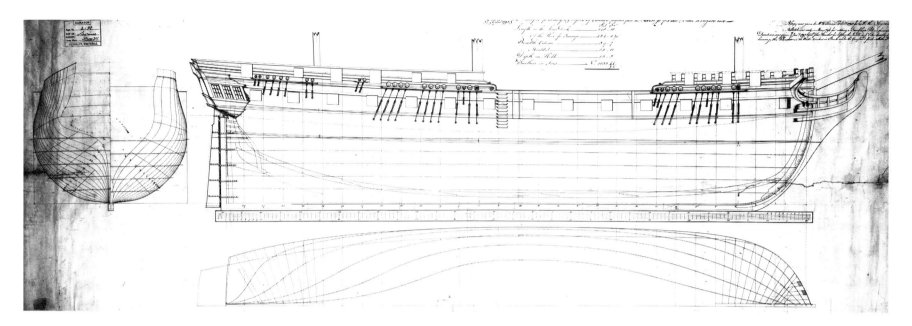

Sirius, 36 guns, design sheer draught, dated 30 September 1795.

This ship retained the hull form of the prototype, *San Fiorenzo*, including the spacing of the ports, but the head and stern were executed in the British style and other fittings and arrangements conformed with Royal Navy practice. Annotations record the addition of a 'bow chase port' (May 1796), and the raising of the forecastle and quarter-deck by 1in and lowering of the waist plansheer 2ins in order to make the gangways flush (Sir John Henslow's directions, 9 January 1797). Note that although the ship adopted the *San Fiorenzo*'s as fitted arrangement of quarterdeck and forecastle gunports, in official lists there is no evidence that the ship carried carronades before 1800. However, the meticulous contemporary historian William James records that the ship carried 44 guns in an action of October 1798, attributing to her the established eight 32pdr carronades of an 18pdr 36. This is possible, but the ship carried two less 9pdrs (hence the 34-gun rating), which casts some doubt on James's assertion that the ship was armed as a standard 36.

Table 27: *NAIAD* CLASS 38-GUN FIFTH RATE
Specification

Armament:	Upper deck	Quarterdeck	Forecastle	Guns	Men
Design	28 x 18pdrs	8 x 9pdrs	2 x 9pdrs	38	284
		4 x 32pdr carr	4 x 32pdr carr		
Changes by AO:					
3 May 1797	9ft guns replace 8ft 18pdrs				
9 May 1797[1]	carr changed to 6 x 32pdr	2 x 32pdr			
Designed by Sir William Rule					

	Lower deck	Keel	Breadth extreme	Depth in hold	Burthen
	ft-ins	ft-ins	ft-ins	ft-ins	tons
Design	147-0	122-8³/₈	39-5	13-9	1014
As completed					
Naiad	147-0	122-6¹/₄	39-5¹/₂	13-9	1020

Notes:

[1] This was as requested by the captain, but there were only six ports a side on the quarterdeck, so it is not easy to see how it was arranged.

Armament changes are listed in Table 60.

the merchant yards, prices the Admiralty refused to countenance.

The strategic situation continued to deteriorate and in April Prussia made peace and withdrew from the First Coalition. At the same time the Navy Board reported that the merchant builders were now offering to contract at up to 10s per ton less than in February, and following a specific enquiry from Cleveley at Gravesend, they asked if they should respond positively to this and similar approaches. The Admiralty seized the opportunity to restore at least some of the programme frustrated in February and ordered a further seven frigates (as well as eight 74s) if builders could be found. All these ships, frigates and battleships, were to be of the largest of their respective classes, and over half of them were based on French prizes. For the frigates, one each was built to the lines of the *Pomone*, *Melpomène*, *Impérieuse* and *San Fiorenzo* and two each to draughts by the Surveyors, Henslow and Rule.

The growing admiration for the apparently more scientific approach to shipbuilding in France has been well documented,[48] but the medium through which that was translated into specific orders is more difficult to attribute. The doctrine of corporate responsibility which guided eighteenth-century public bodies makes it almost impossible to discover individual opinions from official correspondence, but there is considerable circumstantial evidence that Middleton was the inspiration behind the decision to 'copy' French designs. In the 1780s the Navy Board – by his own admission dominated by Middleton – had a free hand in design matters and proposed both the 74s derived from the *Courageux* and the cancelled frigate based on *Prudente*. Once established at the Admiralty, he was even better placed to promote this policy, and it is significant that after he left office new French-derived designs were rare for either frigate or battleship.[49] (The *Leda*, to the lines of the *Hebe*, was actually ordered in April 1796 but was first considered in November 1794, so the design decision may have been made at that point.) However, during his short return to the Admiralty in 1805 as Lord Barham, four individual frigates were again ordered, each to the lines

Table 28: *NAIAD* CLASS 38-GUN FIFTH RATE
Building Data

Name	Ordered	Builder	Laid down	Launched	Sailed	Fitted at	Fate
Naiad	30 Apr 1795	Hill, Limehouse	Sep 1795	27 Feb 1797	6 May 1797	Deptford	Jan 1847 coal hulk; 2 Feb 1866 sold

Table 29: *BOADICEA* CLASS 38-GUN FIFTH RATE
Specification

Armament:	Upper deck	Quarterdeck	Forecastle	Guns	Men
Design	28 x 18pdrs	8 x 9pdrs	2 x 9pdrs	38	284
Changes by AO:					
9 May 1797 added		6 x 32pdr carr	2 x 32pdr carr		
'Similar to *Impérieuse*'					

	Lower deck	Keel	Breadth extreme	Depth in hold	Burthen
	ft-ins	ft-ins	ft-ins	ft-ins	tons
Design	148-6	124-0½	39-8	12-8	1038
As completed					
Boadicea	148-6	123-10½	39-11½	12-8	1052

Armament changes are listed in Table 60.

of a different French prototype. This stands in such marked contrast to the policy of series-building by classes otherwise pursued at the time that it cannot be coincidence.

It remains to be asked why these prototypes were chosen and what Middleton and his Admiralty colleagues expected to gain from this approach. The latter is the more difficult question and in the absence of any surviving discussion of such matters, only a few tentative suggestions can be advanced. The Admiralty was under considerable pressure from Parliament and sea officers to improve British ship design,[50] and seems to have agreed 'that the progressive improvement in the construction and equipment of ships of war in this country has not kept pace with many other countries.'[51] Specifically, the French example was continually quoted as an ideal. There was a distinct feeling

Impérieuse, ex-French, 38 guns, as fitted sheer & profile draught, taken off at Chatham, dated 4 July 1795, and approved by the Admiralty, 13 August 1795.

Although built a few years later this ship was another Coulomb design and very similar to *Minerve* – even the minor differences in hull form might be attributable to slight inaccuracies in taking off the lines. One visible change is the addition of an extra port right forward; the spacing and position suggests a chase port, but it allowed the ship to carry a main battery of twenty-eight 18pdrs. As with *San Fiorenzo* (ex-*Minerve*), little has been done to fit this ship for British requirements, even the main suction pumps being retained, whereas they were normally replaced with chain pumps.

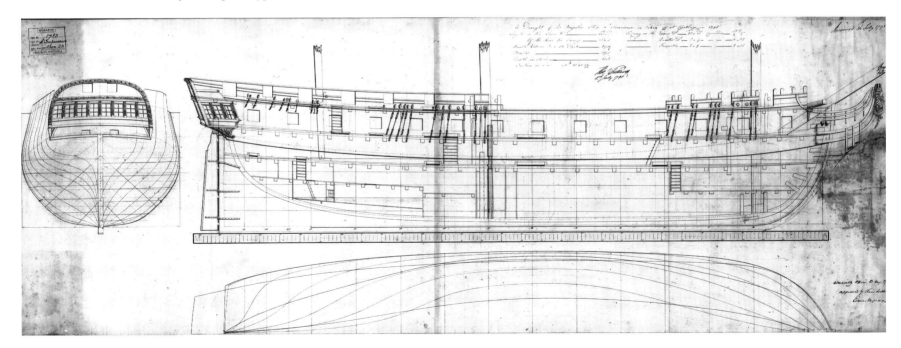

Table 30: *BOADICEA* CLASS 38-GUN FIFTH RATE
Building Data

Name	Ordered	Builder	Laid down	Launched	Sailed	Fitted at	Fate
Boadicea	30 Apr 1795	Adams, Bucklers Hard	Sep 1795	12 Apr 1797	9 Sep 1797	Portsmouth	1854 hulked; May 1858 BU

Table 31: *HYDRA* CLASS 38-GUN FIFTH RATE
Specification

Armament:	Upper deck	Quarterdeck	Forecastle	Guns	Men
Design	28 x 18pdrs	8 x 9pdrs	2 x 9pdrs	38	284
Changes by AO:					
?20 Apr 1796		6 x 32pdr carr	2 x 32pdr carr		
'Similar to *Melpomène*'					

	Lower deck	Keel	Breadth extreme	Depth in hold	Burthen
	ft-ins	ft-ins	ft-ins	ft-ins	tons
Design	148-2	123-7³/₈	39-4	12-8	1017
As completed					
Hydra	148-3	123-7³/₄	39-6¹/₂	12-8	1024

Armament changes are listed in Table 60.

that French warships were 'better' – in as far as this was quantified, it meant frigates being superior sailers and battleships carrying their guns with more freeboard and better stability. The belief was strong among sea officers (particularly those who prided themselves on their 'scientific' understanding of their profession) that this was the product of a greater regard for science which would one day threaten British predominance at sea. Captain Thomas Hamilton, one of a growing band of would-be ship designers in the Navy's officer corps, certainly believed it.[52] The Surveyors, by contrast, were regarded with that peculiarly English sensitivity to class as jumped-up carpenters (which was the first career

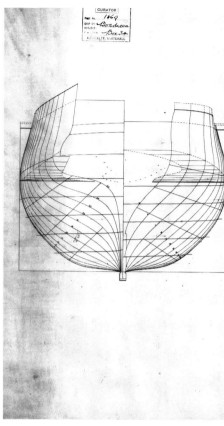

Boadicea, 38 guns, design sheer draught, dated 2 October 1795.

As with *Sirius*, the topsides of the French prototype were modified to British style, while the spacing of the foremost gunport was equalised (in effect, moving it aft by about 4ins) to make it a more effective broadside port. The quarterdeck ports, for both long guns and carronades, follow the positioning of the *Impérieuse* as fitted for British service.

Boadicea, 38 guns, design framing draught, dated 2 November 1795.

This is a standard framing plan for a big frigate of the period. Although employing the dimensions and lines of French ships, the 38s of the 1795 programme were built to British standards, with more substantial scantlings and fastenings. The heavier hull required less ballasting, which would alter the stability and alter the sailing qualities, even if only marginally. From this point of view, imitating the hull forms of French frigates was unlikely to provide usable design lessons.

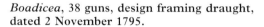
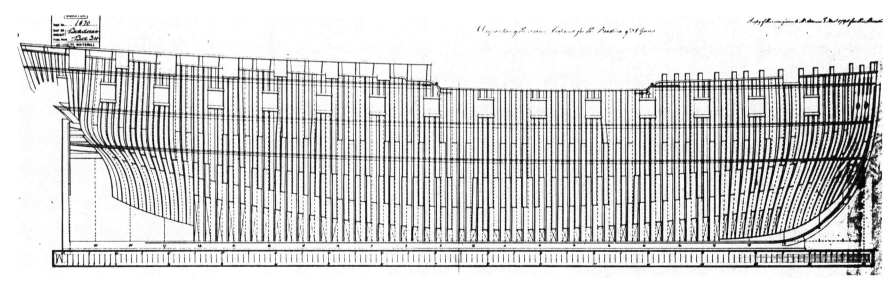

Table 32: *HYDRA* CLASS 38-GUN FIFTH RATE
Building Data

Name	Ordered	Builder	Laid down	Launched	Sailed	Fitted at	Fate
Hydra	30 Apr 1795	Cleveley, Gravesend	Nov 1795	13 Mar 1797	25 Jun 1797	Woolwich	1812 troopship; 13 Jan 1820 sold

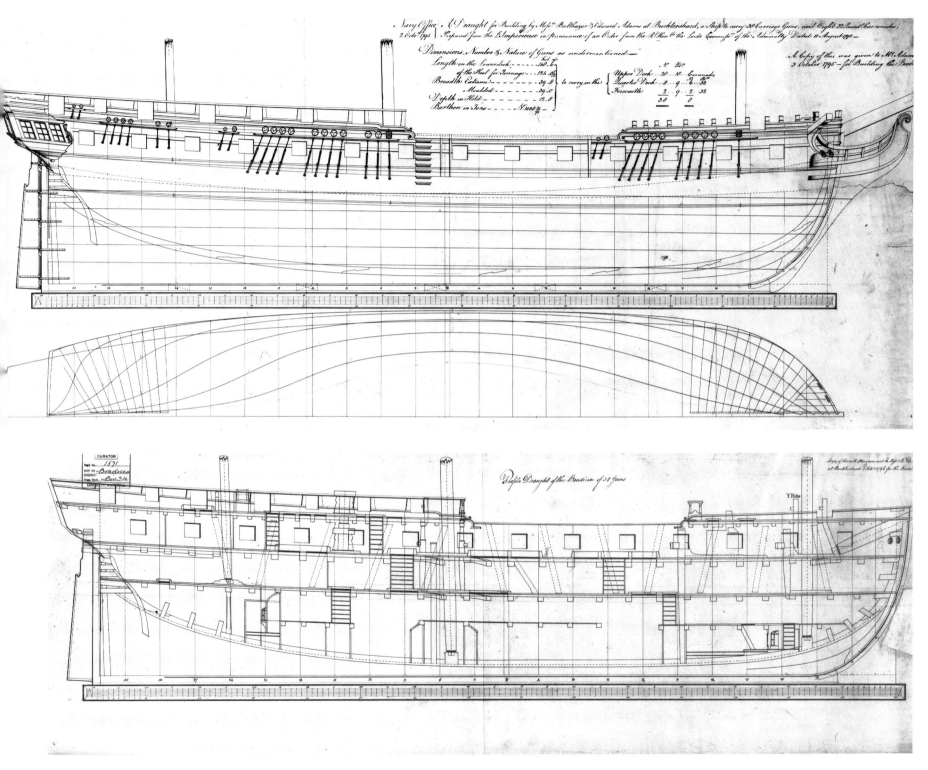

Boadicea, 38 guns, design profile draught, dated 2 February 1796.

As far as was possible with the different proportions of French frigates, the 1795 ships were laid out in the usual Royal Navy manner. Some compromise was inevitable, and *Boadicea*'s low forward magazine was the cause of a complaint from her captain; the Navy Board said it had been made longer by way of compensation. The after powder room was also small by British standards.

step for most of them). As far as sea officers were concerned giving the Surveyors knighthoods did not raise them above the social status of a warrant officer.[53] Hamilton later became embroiled in a bitter argument with the Surveyors over his ideas about naval architecture but was probably expressing a widely held view when he claimed that compared with the Surveyors' 'melancholy proof of ignorance or neglect ... the French proceed with science to system, and that if we cannot get our builders [to] understand them, it is the duty of the Admiralty to copy them...'.[54]

Responding to this kind of pressure, the 1795 programme marked a double departure from existing policy because not only did it espouse enlarged dimensions, but it also adopted the French approach of numerous individual designs to a common specification, rather than series-built classes. In point of fact France was moving towards greater standardisation, based on Sané designs, but the Admiralty was convinced that French frigates were generally singletons. Lord Spencer, for one, could not understand this and in his correspondence with Sidney Smith he quizzed this ingenious officer on the reasons why the French never seemed able to find a design to mass-produce. Smith had no answer but did point out that their large size tended to make French

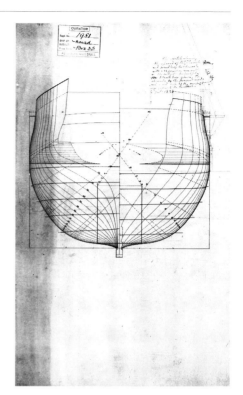

Naiad, 38 guns, design sheer draught, dated 7 May 1795, and approved by the Admiralty, 13 August 1795.

This was Rule's home-grown equivalent of the French-derived frigates of the 1795 programme. Annotations record the alteration to the headrails to incorporate a chase port, and ticked lines also indicate the cutting of the sills for two carronades a side on the forecastle; a further note mentions the addition of 5in to the false keel, by Navy Board warrant to Plymouth, 5 December 1798. On the body plan is a much later sketch showing the spread of the shrouds and the position of the muzzle of a 32pdr, dated 2 July 1828.

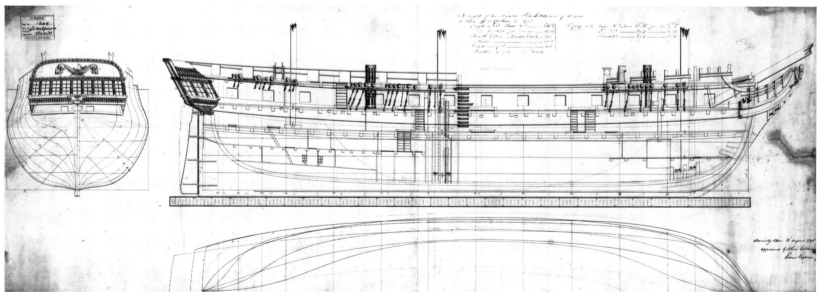

ships superior, whatever their form.[55]

Turning to the 1795 frigates themselves, they were originally all described as 38s, but the *Pomone*-derived ship and Henslow's and Rule's equivalents (*Endymion*, *Cambrian* and *Acasta* respectively) were rated as 40s or 44s and are beyond the scope of this study. Conversely, *San Fiorenzo* had only thirteen usable upper deck ports a side and the *Sirius* based on her became a 36. It may be significant that none of these ships was taken in a single-ship action by an opponent of equal force, so they may have appeared more formidable than further experience was to reveal. This was particularly true of *Pomone* (armed with 24pdrs) for which there was no equivalent in the Royal Navy, but there were soon

Melpomène, ex-French, 38 guns, as fitted sheer & profile draught, taken off at Chatham and approved by the Admiralty, 13 August 1795.

Another Coulomb design and very like, if not an exact sister of, *Minerve* and *Impérieuse*, the dimensions of all three ships being well within the tolerances expected of British ships built to a single draught. The taffrail is raked aft more than the other two, but the ship is otherwise similar. French features have again beeen retained, but the addition of what may be a small hanging magazine forward is interesting. The ship was fitted with an orlop platform by Admiralty Order of 2 April 1799.

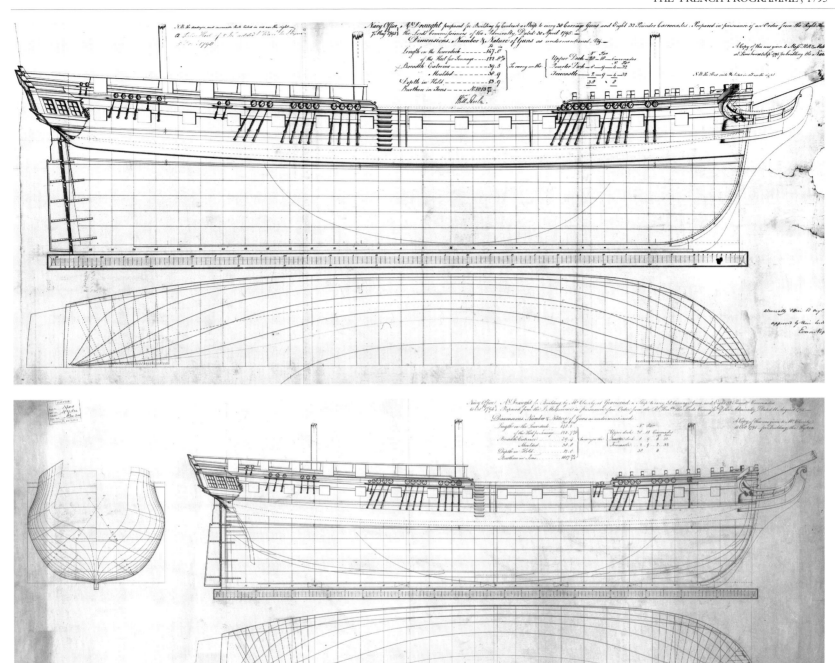

Hydra, 38 guns, design sheer draught, dated 15 October 1795.

Like the other two 'French copies', this ship was given a typically British finish above the waterline, but in all three the relatively large angle of tumble-home was inherited from the prototypes. This was in distinct contrast to British-designed ships of the period, which were becoming more wall-sided.

to be so many cases of British frigates taking French opponents of nominally greater force that no more 24pdr armed ships were deemed necessary until the American War of 1812. This overwhelming superiority in action also reduced the pressure to build very large 18pdr ships, although it is interesting that even in 1795 ships of 148ft on the lower deck were chosen as model 38s, even though 150ft and 152ft examples were available (*Amethyst* and *Arethuse* respectively).

It may be coincidence but all three prototypes for the 18pdr ships were the work of J M B Coulomb, who had retired in 1792 as *ingénieur directeur* at Rochefort and may be seen as an older and more conservative influence on French design. Certainly the future (for both

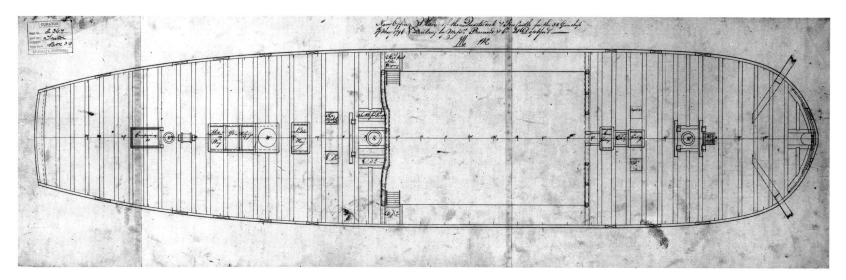

Triton, 32 guns, design quarterdeck & forecastle draught, dated 17 May 1796.

The unusual bow configuration produced a very blunt forecastle deck, which allowed a pair of chase ports to point directly forward. On neither the forecastle nor the upper deck was there a broadside gun position much ahead of the fore mast, as was traditionally the case with fine-lined French frigates.

navies) lay with the work of Sané, but it may be that Coulomb's somewhat fuller hull form exerted greater initial appeal to British sensibilities. They were not subjected to any systematic trials and, indeed, none of the chosen prototypes had seen much British service before the decision was made to imitate them. *Impérieuse* was clearly a fast ship, but was only at her best in light winds and was always wet. *Melpomène* was closer to traditional British requirements, being a good windward performer (particularly in heavy weather), but it was judged that 'her sailing is good but not very superior, except in a stiff gale and heavy sea'. Like many French ships, both were long in wearing; and neither could stow more than four months' provisions under hatches. *San Fiorenzo* was not a particularly outstanding performer under sail but if a 36 of 148ft was required she was the only available French model.[56]

Although the *Boadicea*, *Hydra* and *Sirius* copied the lines of the French ships they were undoubtedly built to Royal Dockyard standards of scantlings and fastening, resulting in a heavier hull. This is evident in the extra ballast required to bring the French ships to the same marks as their British 'clones'.[57] They were never as highly regarded as their French models, and were subtly at odds with Royal Navy requirements: when Captain Keats complained of the inadequate size of his ship's magazine it must have given the Navy Board a certain pleasure to point out to Their Lordships that the *Boadicea* 'was built by admiralty direction after the *Impérieuse* so the hold is shallow and the magazine low'.[58]

The Surveyors' own efforts were not very impressive either. Henslow simply proffered another *Artois* class, the *Ethalion*, but Rule designed an expanded version of his *Amazon* which became the *Naiad*. This ship was the first British-designed 38 to achieve 7ft between the gunports, but only by carrying guns a long way forward and right aft, with the result that the ship was always known as a heavy pitcher. In complete contrast to ships like *Impérieuse*, she was best in strong winds under a press of sail when she could touch 13kts. In most conditions she did not compare with other frigates – St Vincent, for example, thought her inferior to *Hussar* or *Dryad*[59] – but was roomy, stowing six months' provisions with ease, and was both weatherly and a good sea-boat.

Triton, 32 guns, design sheer draught, approved by the Admiralty, 7 April 1796.

Gambier's experimental frigate was eventually completed with 12pdrs, but was originally conceived as an 18pdr ship. Some of Gambier's ideas – the flat sheer, overhanging bow, and wall sides – were to resurface in other classes, suggesting that his design influence was wider than previously suspected.

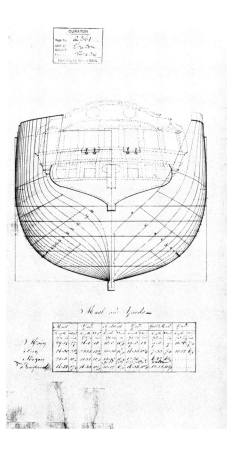

5. *Small Ships and Experiments*

The 1795 programme of French 'copies' was not an unqualified success, and after Middleton left the Admiralty there was no desire to perpetuate any of these designs. However, his departure did not signal the end of innovation, and if anything Lord Spencer's administration seemed even more inclined to experiment. Middleton had been a strong supporter of Samuel Bentham, now appointed Inspector-General of Naval Works, who was permitted to build four schooners and two amazing double-ended sloops to his own designs.[60] Simultaneously, Captain Schank's ideas regarding sliding keels and radical gun carriage designs were being tested, while potentially most revolutionary of all was the Admiralty's support for Lord Stanhope's *Kent Ambinavigator*, which had it worked, would have become the world's first steam-powered warship. These were relatively small craft but in 1796 the Admiralty sent the Navy Board the design for an extremely unusual frigate, without any reference to its provenance.

This vessel was built very quickly of fir and launched as the *Triton*.[61] The Admiralty was almost consciously mysterious about the ship's designer, which may have been embarrassment since it was one of their own members, James Gambier. A few years later the *Naval Chronicle* pointed out that the ship was 'built on Admiral Gambier's improved plan',[62] and his pride in his creation can be gauged from his commission-ing a portrait of the ship from Nicholas Pocock, a leading marine artist of the day.[63] The Admiral was also responsible for the model, currently in the National Maritime Museum, which was inherited by his nephew Vice-Admiral Robert Gambier and later presented to the Royal Hospital collection. James Gambier, who was Middleton's nephew, succeeded him at the Admiralty and was regarded as a close ally by their service enemies.[64] His interest in naval architecture was noted later,[65] and he was also credited with the design of the 74-gun *Plantagenet*,[66] although the ship is usually listed as the work of Sir William Rule, so Gambier may have been little more than the inspiration for this large two-decker without a poop.

Triton was built with a view to economy of timber and improved sailing qualities. On the former head, it was said that 'the country will be much indebted to Admiral Gambier for this experiment, as she will be built of straighter timber than any ship of her class ever was in this or any other country, a very valuable acquisition at a time when compass timber is so very difficult to obtain ...'[67] Although never previously executed so rigorously, the concept was not entirely original and in this respect the ship exhibits the influence of Samuel Bentham, particularly in the flat sheer, lack of tumblehome and steeply raked bow, features found in his *Dart* and *Arrow*.[68] The ship incorporated one other innovation which was the working of the toptimbers to provide 'air pipes' to ventilate the lower deck, the berthing deck on a frigate which usually had little more than small scuttles for air.

continued on page 49

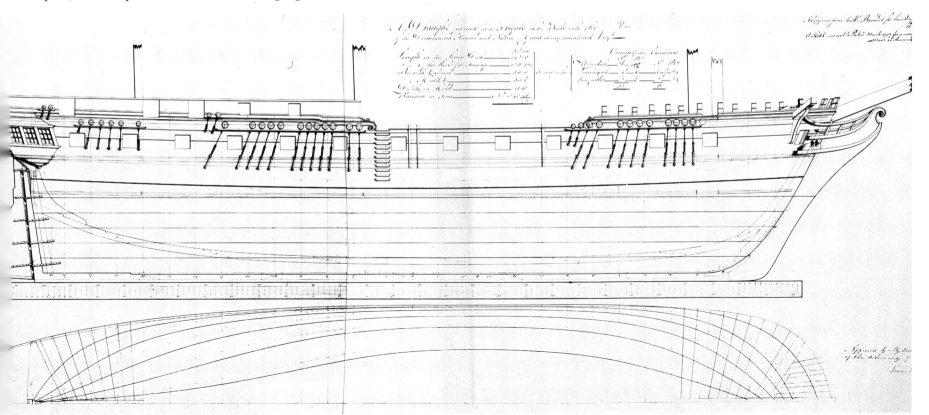

Table 33: *AMPHION* CLASS 32-GUN FIFTH RATES
Specification

Armament:	Upper deck	Quarterdeck	Forecastle	Guns	Men
Design					
(16 Dec 1796)	26 x 18pdrs	4 x 6pdrs,	2 x 6pdrs,	32	254
		4 x 24pdr carr	2 x 24pdr carr		
Changes by AO:					
cMar 1800 (*Aeolus/Medusa*)		2 x 6pdrs,	2 x 6pdrs,		
		8 x 24pdr carr	2 x 24pdr carr		

Designed by Sir William Rule

	Lower deck	Keel	Breadth extreme	Depth in hold	Burthen
	ft-ins	ft-ins	ft-ins	ft-ins	tons
Design	144-0	121-1½	37-6	12-6	906
As completed					
Amphion	144-0½	121-6⅞	37-7¼	12-6	914
Medusa	144-0	121-6	37-8½	12-5½	920
Aeolus	144-3	121-9	37-8	21-6	919

Armament changes are listed in Table 60.

Amphion, 32 guns, design sheer draught, dated 24 June 1796.

Although the midship section is similar to all of Rule's frigates, it is known that the Admiralty interfered in the design of this ship. Although by no means as extreme as *Triton*, the ship has a noticeably flat sheer and raking bow, both features favoured by Gambier.

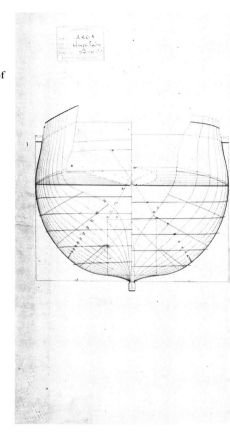

Triton, 32 guns, design upper deck draught, dated 17 May 1796.

Even on the upper deck, the chase ports can bear nearly directly ahead.

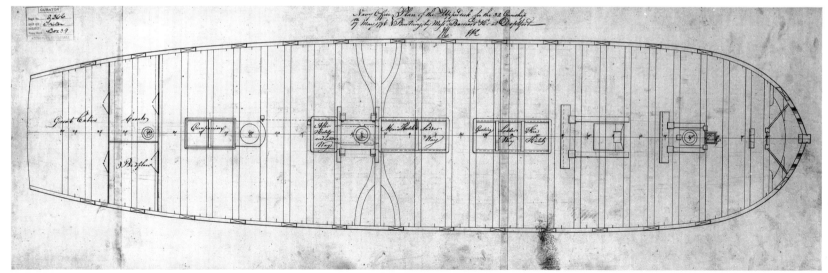

Table 34: *AMPHION* CLASS 32-GUN FIFTH RATES
Building Data

Name	Ordered	Builder	Laid down	Launched	Sailed	Fitted at	Fate
Amphion	11 Jun 1796	Betts, Mistleythorn	Jul 1796	19 Mar 1798	6 Jul 1798	Chatham	1812 troopship; Nov 1820 became breakwater
Aeolus	28 Jan 1800	Barnard, Deptford	Apr 1800	28 Feb 1801	10 Apr 1801	Deptford	Oct 1817 BU
Medusa	28 Jan 1800	Pitcher, Northfleet	Apr 1800	14 Apr 1801	26 Jun 1801	Woolwich	1813 hulk; Nov 1816 BU

Note: A further two of this class were ordered in 1805.

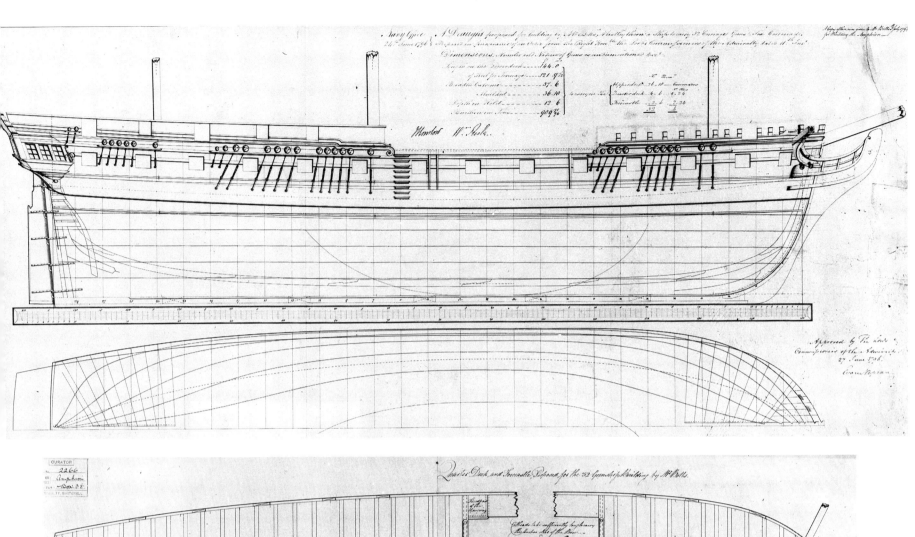

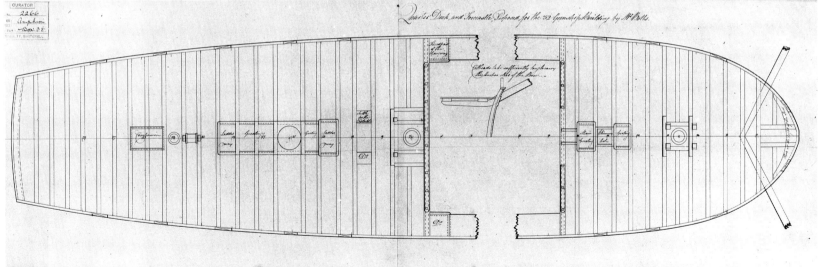

Amphion, 32 guns, 1796, design quarterdeck & forecastle draught.

Compared with *Triton*, the forecastle shape is more acute, but the forward-facing chase ports are similar.

Table 35: *NARCISSUS* CLASS 32-GUN FIFTH RATES
Specification

Armament:	Upper deck	Quarterdeck	Forecastle	Guns	Men
Design	26 x 18pdrs[1]	4 x 6pdrs, 6 x 24pdr carr	2 x 6pdrs, 2 x 24pdr carr	32	254
Changes by AO:					
20 Jun 1801		2 x 9pdrs,[2] 8 x 24pdr carr	2 x 9pdrs, 2 x 24pdr carr		

Designed by Sir John Henslow

	Lower deck ft-ins	Keel ft-ins	Breadth extreme ft-ins	Depth in hold ft-ins	Burthen tons
Design	142-0	118-5	37-6	12-6	886
As completed					
Narcissus	142-0½	118-4⅞	37-8	12-6	894
Tartar	142-0	118-3½	37-8½	12-6	895

Notes:

[1] The *Narcissus* was intended to test Gover's short 24pdrs and was ordered to be so fitted on 11 Jun 1800. However, the ports proved too small to allow the guns any real elevation and on 24 Jul 1801 it was decided to supply 18pdrs instead, so the ship never cruised with 24pdrs.

[2] The AO relates specifically to the quarterdeck armament, but it would be curious if the forecastle long guns remained 6pdrs.

Armament changes in service are listed in Table 60.

Later *Amphion* class 32, revised sheer draught, dated 1 February 1800.

This draught was used for the *Medusa* and *Aeolus*, and with further modifications, for two ships in 1805. A note says it was prepared from the *Amphion*'s draught with alterations to the quarterdeck ports, the head, and the barricading of the forecastle. The secondary armament for the *Medusa* and *Aeolus* comprised a 6pdr long gun and 24pdr carronade on each side of the forecastle, and a 6pdr and eight 24s per side on the quarterdeck.

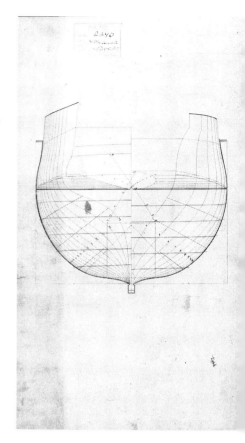

Amphion, 32 guns, 1796, design upper deck draught.

On the upper deck, *Amphion*'s more pointed plan at the bow made it impossible to contrive chase ports which could fire directly forward.

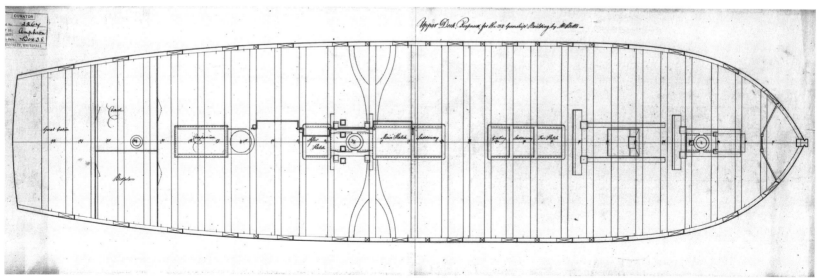

Table 36: *NARCISSUS* CLASS 32-GUN FIFTH RATES
Building Data

Name	Ordered	Builder	Laid down	Launched	Sailed	Fitted at	Fate
Narcissus	13 Jan 1798	Deptford Dyd	Feb 1800	12 May 1801	2 Jul 1801	Deptford	1823 convict hulk and hospital; Jan 1837 sold
Tartar	28 Jan 1800	Brindley, Frindsbury	Aug 1800	27 Jun 1801	18 Jul 1801	Chatham	18 Aug 1811 wrecked

Note: A further three (two cancelled) of this class were ordered in 1805-6.

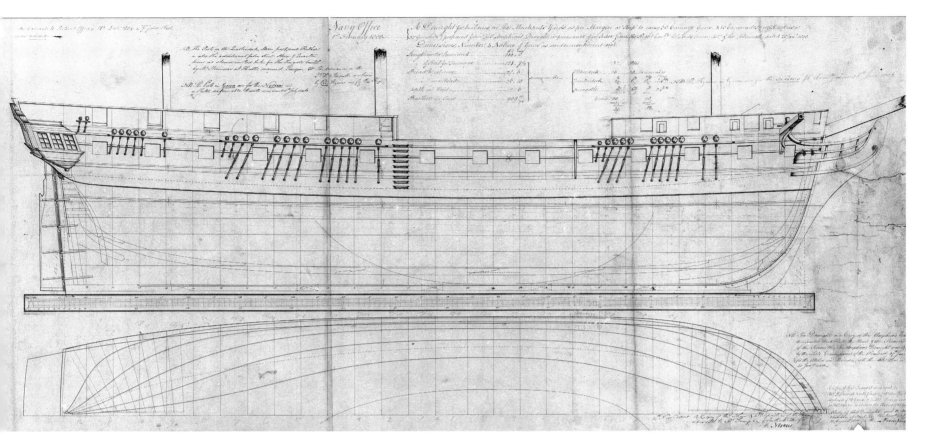

With regard to fast sailing, Gambier was clearly anxious to see his ship proven and John Gore, *Triton*'s captain, was ordered to report in detail on her performance. The speed with which the Admiralty passed on Gore's report to the Navy Board suggests that they felt the experiment to be entirely justified.[69] Set out like a Sailing Quality form it shows that the ship had some obvious advantages, but to the objective eye, some nasty drawbacks. The ship was undoubtedly fast,[70] Gore claiming 'we have fore-reached on everything we have met with'. In October 1799 the captains of HM Ships *Alcmene*, *Naiad* and *Ethalion* were given an expensive lesson on this score when in pursuit of the Spanish treasure frigates *Santa Brigada* and *Thetis*; the *Triton* came from nowhere to claim a share of one of the biggest prize hauls of all time, each captain receiving over £40,000, more than twice the value of the ship he commanded. However, *Triton* was not weatherly, and with a huge weight of ballast, rolled very deep, although easy; she did not pitch much but the peculiar form of her bow with its great flare caused her to slam. Gore was asked specifically about the defects or inconveniences attributable to the peculiar construction of the ship and his comments are worth quoting in full.

> She dips deep abaft owing to the fineness of her run and the peculiar form of her bow which is apt to throw her down by the stern and I fear would make her a dangerous ship to scud in a hard gale and high sea – her being fir obliges her to have a vast quantity of iron ballast – viz 200 tons and 100 tons shingle which occasions her to roll

deep; otherwise she is the easiest ship I have ever known. The form of her bow prevents her falling into the sea but she strikes hard and I fear it may occasion her being worn out sooner than if her form was more like other ships, but still it has its advantages in keeping her very dry and giving a vast deal of room on both decks, and I think helps her to windward when carrying sail at sea.

The captain and surgeon were also asked their opinion of the contribution made by the ventilation to the health of the crew.

> The Air Tubes are the best thing I have ever known and I am confident have contributed greatly to the health of the people as they promote a wonderful circulation of air and does away totally [with] that thick noxious foul air which is always felt between decks in a frigate when the people and hammocks are below.

The captain was correct in his assessment of the short life of the ship, and at best the verdict on the hull form was 'not proven' but the cautious would have regarded it as dangerously flawed. On the other hand the 'air pipes' were clearly a success and the Admiralty ordered them included in all future frigates 'if it can be done without detriment to their frames'.[71]

The Admiralty's attention remained fixed on large frigates and in June 1796 was considering draughts not only by the Surveyors but also a design by their French emigré Second Assistant, Barrallier; Their Lordships also requested sight of the *Pomone* draught. By going behind the backs of his superiors Barrallier persuaded the Admiralty to try his

Table 37: *ETHALION* CLASS 36-GUN FIFTH RATE
Specification

Armament:	Upper deck	Quarterdeck	Forecastle	Guns	Men
Design (7 Sep 1799)	26 x 18pdrs	14 x 32pdr carr	2 x 9pdr, 4 x 32pdr carr	36	264
Designed by 'Admiralty'					

	Lower deck	Keel	Breadth extreme	Depth in hold	Burthen
	ft-ins	ft-ins	ft-ins	ft-ins	tons
Design	152-0	129-2¼	38-0	13-0	992
As completed *Ethalion*	152-5½	129-7¾	38-0	13-0	996

Note: Probably designed by Gambier.

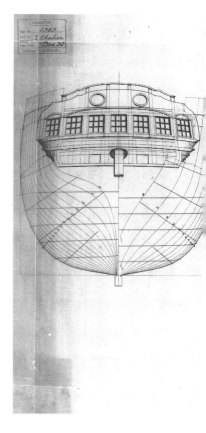

Ethalion, 36 guns, design sheer draught, approved by the Admiralty, 5 September 1799.

Another anonymous 'Admiralty' design, but bearing the hallmarks of Gambier's design beliefs – flat sheer, wall sides, and a less extreme form of *Triton*'s bow. In this ship the carronade finally achieved the apogee of its development, usurping all but two long chase guns on the upperworks.

design instead of the proposed 38, the result being a big 44 to be built at Milford called the *Lavinia*. However, one of the merchant builders touting for business was Betts of Mistleythorn and although the original intention was to allocate a 38 to him, the Navy Board had to point out that the depth of water on the Stour would allow nothing bigger than a 32. It is likely that the 32-gun ship would have been given up at this point, but like the 28 in the American War, it continued to be built in order to use capacity that would otherwise lie idle.[72] Most of the relatively few succeeding orders can be put down to similar physical or logistical restrictions.

Anticipating the go-ahead, Rule had a design prepared, but the Admiralty sent it back covered in alterations. The length was increased to 144ft; the rake of the stem profile was increased, and a chase port added; the lower height of breadth was raised 18in; and the lines in the run were made finer.[73] This level of detailed interference was a novelty,

Narcissus class 32, design sheer draught, dated 9 January 1798.

These ships underwent many minor modifications, some of which are recorded on this draught. The chase port was altered in the *Narcissus*, while in the *Tartar* the angle of the whole headrail-cathead assembly was changed; one quarterdeck 6pdr was replaced by a 24pdr carronade so the second port from forward was enlarged, by order of 24 November 1800.

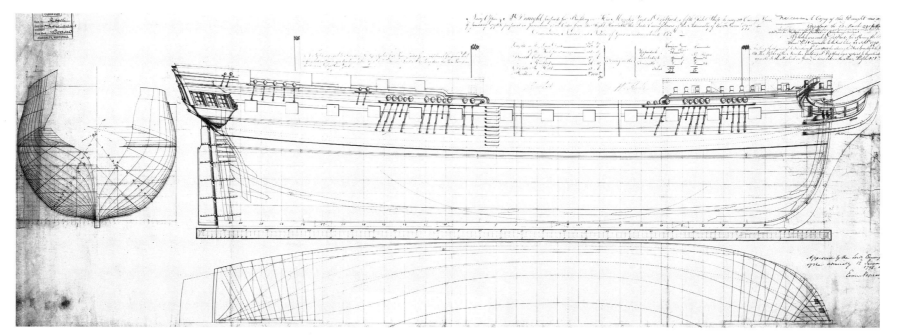

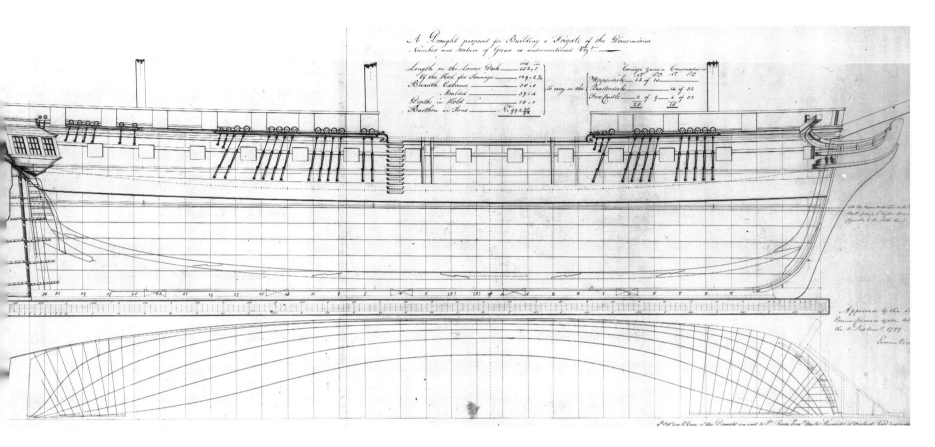

and although Rule was the junior Surveyor he must have found it mortifying. The modifications, presumably down to Gambier's influence, show striking similarities with ideas behind the *Triton* ordered a month earlier: the extra length gave the ship the greatest length:breadth ratio of any frigate so far designed by the Surveyors, and the raked bow owes something to *Triton*'s most individual feature. Contrary to accepted wisdom this design-by-committee produced not a camel but a racehorse – in service the *Amphion* proved fast, weatherly and manoeuvrable, and was particularly good in strong winds.

Very few 18pdr 32s were built in this period – one each in 1796 and 1798 and three in 1800 – and there were usually specific reasons unrelated to the qualities of the design for these orders. The next 32, for example, was earmarked for a specific slip and to use available small timber at Deptford. The Dockyard was hampered as a building yard by having two slips launching into a basin with a narrow entrance to the river, and therefore could not build the largest frigates on these slips (although 36s were constructed inside the basin later). In keeping with the dual Surveyorship philosophy, Henslow designed an equivalent to the *Amphion* for the Deptford ship, which became the *Narcissus*. She was shorter, although otherwise similar in dimensions; slower than *Amphion*, the ship was never regarded as among the navy's best sailers, but was weatherly, manoeuvrable and a good sea-boat.

British frigates were becoming relatively longer in the late 1790s and there is circumstantial evidence to suggest that the development was conscious and being driven by the Admiralty rather than the Surveyors.[74] *Triton* was an extreme manifestation of this policy, being longer and shallower, and much closer in proportions to French frigates, than any indigenous design. However, reports had demonstrated that the ship was not without faults, and in 1799 the Admiralty produced another of its 'own' designs. This ship, the second *Ethalion*, was the largest 36-gun frigate of the period and the most expensive 'experiment'; with a length:breadth ratio of 4.0 she was also the longest and shallowest frigate so far built in Britain. In general, she was a less extreme version of the *Triton*, with a less acutely overhanging bow, nearly flat sheer and a wall-sided hull with midship section that resembled *Triton*'s but was less sharp. One other claim to fame was that *Ethalion* was the first frigate

Table 38: *ETHALION* CLASS 36-GUN FIFTH RATE
Building Data

Name	Ordered	Builder	Laid down	Launched	Sailed	Fitted at	Fate
Ethalion	7 Sep 1799	Woolwich Dyd	May 1800	29 Jul 1802	25 Oct 1802	Woolwich	1823 convict ship; 1824 receiving ship; 1835 breakwater at Harwich

designed from the outset for an all-carronade armament, less two chase guns, on the upperworks – official correspondence referred to 'a frigate of 28 carriage guns and 18 carronades'.[75]

Because the Admiralty which ordered her had left office before she was completed, there was no rush to discover *Ethalion*'s characteristics, but when St Vincent's Board was replaced with Melville's – and Gambier regained influence[76] – Captain Lord Stuart was ordered to report in October 1804. The ship exhibited less dramatic characteristics than *Triton*, although the value of her bow when riding at anchor was noted. She was reasonably fast and weatherly, generally an easy sea-boat – although her great length caused straining in the short seas of her North Sea station – and carried her guns 8ft from the water with four months' stores. The major drawback was the ease with which she lay over to the top of the wales, although she could then carry a press of sail without further heeling. When heeled it was difficult to elevate the lee guns sufficiently and the captain was worried about the prospects of engaging to leeward; but he also felt that the gun carriages were too tall and that adequate elevation might be possible if the guns were lowered in the carriages.[77] This cannot have been effective since the problem was still causing concern as late as 1815.[78]

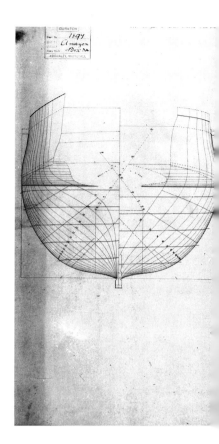

Amazon class 38, design draught, dated 19 April 1796.

Rule's 150ft 38 was subject to an 18-month delay, although two ships were eventually built to this design. It was also proposed as the 38 to be built by Jacobs at Milford Haven (Admiralty Order of 16 December 1796), but this ship was built to a larger design by the French emigré Second Assistant Surveyor Barrallier. All the quarter-deck ports except the foremost were altered to take carronades (Admiralty Order of 1 June 1799). The design of the head was also changed, as depicted in pencil, so that the cathead was further aft and the chase port cut through its supporter (this was as built); this change seems to have been inspired by the desire to have fore-castle chase positions bearing right ahead. Although not apparent on the sheer, the framing draught (dated later: 13 May 1796) shows oarports and a berthed up forecastle.

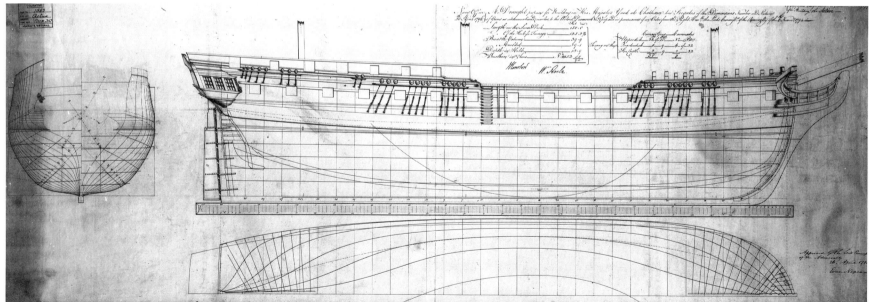

Active, 38 guns, design sheer draught, dated 25 April 1796.

Henslow's contribution to the new 150ft 38 was essentially an enlarged *Artois*, with the addition of a chase port in the extra length forward of the upper deck battery. The draught was produced in response to an Admiralty Order of 6 November 1794 and mentions two ships; the order was suspended and one ship may have been replaced by the *Leda*.

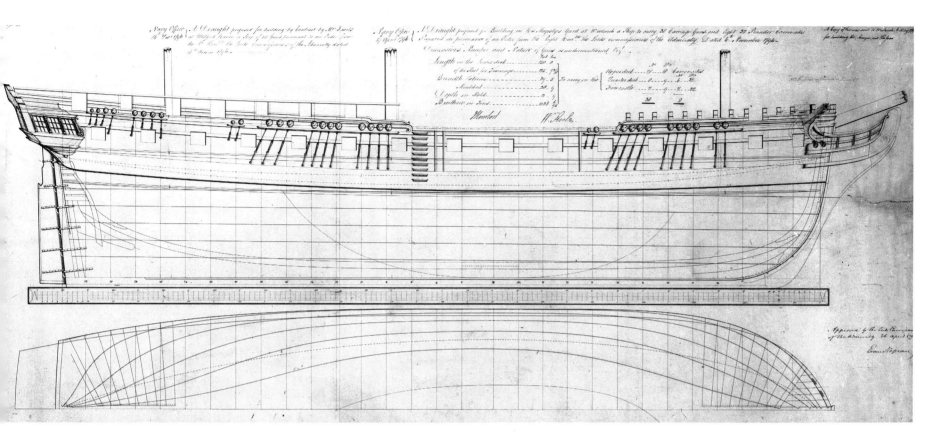

6. The Big Ship Era, 1796-1800

After Middleton left the Admiralty the pace of new construction had noticeably slackened. This did not indicate any easing of the strategic situation, because Spain joined France in 1796 and even the dogged Austrians made peace in 1797. Furthermore, between 1793 and the end of 1795 the French navy had added no less than twenty new 18pdr ships (although thereafter new building was reduced to a trickle). In Britain, relationships between the merchant builders and the Admiralty were soured in 1796, followed by a financial crisis in 1797, and for a few years there was greater reliance on the Royal Dockyards for frigate-building. Furthermore, large numbers of prizes continued to swell the Navy List – seventeen large frigates were captured between 1793 and 1801, exactly the same number as 38s built. Middleton later

Table 39: *ACTIVE* CLASS 38-GUN FIFTH RATE
Specification

Armament:	Upper deck	Quarterdeck	Forecastle	Guns	Men
Design	28 x 18pdrs	8 x 9pdrs	2 x 9pdrs	38	284
Changes by AO:					
6 May 1797 added		6 x 32pdr carr	2 x 32pdr carr		
15 Jan 1800		2 x 9pdrs,	2 x 9pdrs,		
		12 x 32pdr carr	4 x 32pdr carr		

Designed by Sir John Henslow (modified *Artois* class)

	Lower deck ft-ins	Keel ft-ins	Breadth extreme ft-ins	Depth in hold ft-ins	Burthen tons
Design	150-0	125-2⅞	39-9	13-9	1053
As completed					
Active	150-0	125-2	39-10½	13-9	1058

Armament changes are listed in Table 60.

Table 40: *ACTIVE* CLASS 38-GUN FIFTH RATE
Building Data

Name	Ordered	Builder	Laid down	Launched	Sailed	Fitted at	Fate
Active	27 Apr 1796[1]	Chatham Dyd	Jul 1798	14 Dec 1799	4 Feb 1800	Chatham	1825 hulk; 1833 renamed *Argo*; Oct 1860 BU

Note:

[1] The Admiralty originally announced its intention to build three 38s on 6 Nov 1794 but the order to proceed was withheld until the date given above; the other two ships were *Amazon* and *Leda*.

Table 41: *AMAZON* CLASS 38-GUN FIFTH RATES
Specification

Armament:	Upper deck	Quarterdeck	Forecastle	Guns	Men
Design	28 x 18pdrs	8 x 9pdrs	2 x 9pdrs	38	284
Changes by AO:					
6 May 1797 added		6 x 32pdr carr	2 x 32pdr carr		
6 Jun & 2 Jul 1799 (*Amazon*)		12 x 32pdr carr	2 x 32pdr carr		
		2 x 9pdrs	2 x 9pdrs		
17 Jun 1799 (*Hussar*)		As *Amazon*			
Designed by Sir William Rule					

	Lower deck	Keel	Breadth extreme	Depth in hold	Burthen
	ft-ins	ft-ins	ft-ins	ft-ins	tons
Design	150-0	125-7³⁄₈	39-5	13-9	1038
As completed					
Amazon	150-0	125-7³⁄₈	39-5	13-9	1038
Hussar, (ex-*Hyena*)	150-3	125-8	39-6	13-9	1043

Armament changes are listed in Table 60.

Table 42: *AMAZON CLASS* 38-GUN FIFTH RATES
Building Data

Name	Ordered	Builder	Laid down	Launched	Sailed	Fitted at	Fate
Amazon	27 Apr 1796[1]	Woolwich Dyd	Apr 1796	18 May 1799	5 Jul 1799	Woolwich	May 1817 BU
Hussar (ex-*Hyena*)[2]	15 Feb 1797	Woolwich Dyd	Aug 1798	1 Jun 1799	11 Nov 1799	Woolwich	8 Feb 1804 wrecked

Notes:

[1] The Admiralty originally announced its intentions to build three 38s on 6 Nov 1794 but the order to proceed was withheld until the date given above; the other two ships were *Active* and *Leda*. A second *Amazon* class ship was proposed by the Navy Board in response to the AO of 16 Dec 1796 for a 38-gun ship, but it was not approved, Barrallier's design being preferred (*Lavinia*).

[2] By AO 24 Jan 1798.

Table 43: *LEDA* CLASS 38-GUN FIFTH RATE
Specification

Armament:	Upper deck	Quarterdeck	Forecastle	Guns	Men
Design					
(6 May 1797)	28 x 18pdrs	8 x 9pdrs,	2 x 9pdrs,		
		6 x 32pdr carr	2 x 32pdr carr		
Changes by AO:					
15 Jan 1800		2 x 9pdrs,	2 x 9pdrs,		
		12 x 32pdr carr	4 x 32pdr carr		
'Similar to the *Hebe*					

	Lower deck	Keel	Breadth extreme	Depth in hold	Burthen
	ft-ins	ft-ins	ft-ins	ft-ins	tons
Design	150-1¹⁄₂	125-4⁷⁄₈	39-11	12-9	1063
As completed					
Leda	150-2	125-4	40-1	12-9	1071

Armament changes are listed in Table 60.

criticised the Spencer and St Vincent administrations for not building enough, calculating that ten frigates per year should be laid down in merchant yards just to preserve the existing size of the navy. He was adamant that the Royal Dockyards should be reserved for repairs and refits and that prizes simply compounded the long-term problem, 'especially since so large [a] proportion of our present fleet consists in ships captured from the enemy, which experience has proved are not so lasting as those of our own build...'.[79] It was probably his influence which prevented the three frigates earmarked for Dockyard slips in November 1794 from being laid down, but they were finally ordered as 38s in April 1796.

Each of these ships was built to a different draught, like the previous year's programme, but only one was of French origin. A lower deck length of 148ft had proved a little too small and these ships moved up to 150ft, a standard that was to prove satisfactory for thirty-five years. However, although the length was increased, breadth and depth remained much the same as earlier British-derived 38s. Henslow modified his existing *Artois* design for the *Active*, preserving the port spacing but using the extra length beyond the end of the battery, in an

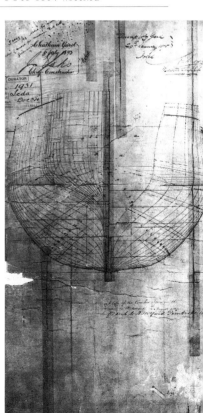

Leda class 38, design sheer draught, dated 1 June 1796.

This much annotated and altered sheer draught incorporates many of the changes applied to this very large class, including postwar developments like the circular stern. *Leda* herself was the only member of the class designed with the open forecastle and a mixed quarterdeck armament of guns and carronades; she also had the lower, curved headrails shown. The design was 'prepared from the *Hebe*, by Admiralty Order of 27 April last', one modification being the chase port, for which the gunport arrangement of the French ship allowed little space.

Table 44: *LEDA* CLASS 38-GUN FIFTH RATE
Building Data

Name	Ordered	Builder	Laid down	Launched	Sailed	Fitted at	Fate
Leda	27 Apr 1796[1]	Chatham Dockyard	1 May 1799	18 Nov 1800	19 Dec 1800	Chatham	31 Jan 1808 wrecked

Notes:

This ship was the prototype for a very large class: thirty-eight more were launched 1802-1830 (plus two cancelled in 1831) and a further eight were built of fir to a slightly modified design in 1812-13.

[1] The Admiralty announced its intention to build three 38s on 6 Nov 1794, but the order to proceed was withheld until the above date (the draught was prepared in response to this later order, so the design was not decided in 1794). The other two ships became the *Active* and *Amazon*.

attempt to reduce the pitching of the earlier ships. In this he was successful, and the ship proved marginally faster than the *Artois* class, although she was rather leewardly. Rule also modified an existing design, his *Amazon* being similar to the *Naiad* with the extra length worked in forward of the battery. This did not entirely eradicate the problem of pitching – and in fact the ship was characterised in general as a very uneasy sea-boat – but she was fast, weatherly and powerful under sail.

The third design, which became the *Leda*, was based on the famous *Hebe*, captured in 1782, so the Navy had plenty of experience with the ship. One of the first French 18pdr frigates, this Sané design was the basis of the standard French 40-gun ship and the *Leda* herself became the prototype of the largest frigate class ever built for the Royal Navy, both services adding to the class until well after the Napoleonic War.[80] In the circumstances, therefore, one would expect outstanding charac-

teristics from the ship. Strictly speaking, the ship had none, but the design proves that good all-round attributes are of more value in naval service than notable superiority in one or two areas. This is not to say that the design was mediocre: many British frigates carried their batteries higher and stowed six months' provisions with greater ease, but the ship was without serious vices and could fulfil all the functions of frigate perfectly. This kind of unspectacular excellence takes a long time to manifest itself, and no sister for *Leda* was ordered for six years. Even when the design was ordered in numbers from 1808, a larger 154ft class was built in parallel, so it was never truly *the* standard design; but whereas a new large 38 was built from 1813, the *Leda*s went on until 1832.

The enlarged and faster battleships of 1795-96 have been associated with Howe's policy of distant blockade, in which the Channel Fleet was kept in sheltered home waters to be released in pursuit of the enemy once

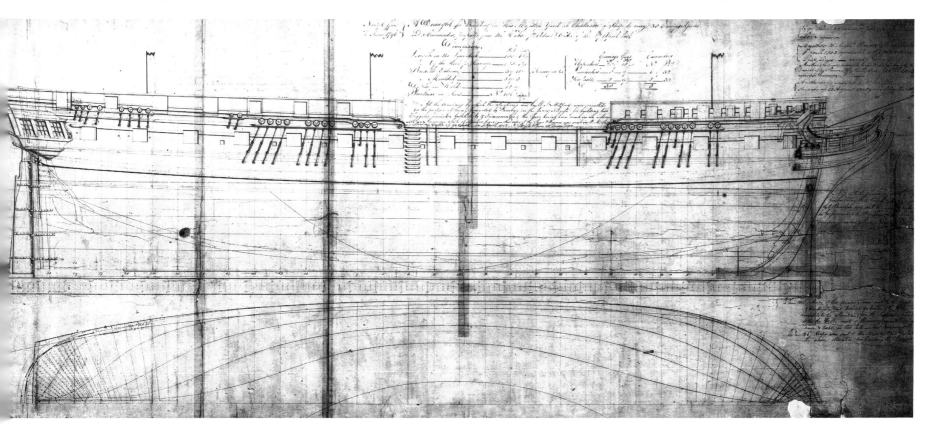

they were known to be out.[81] This placed extra stress on the frigates of the inshore squadrons of observation, which had to be large enough to counter any likely French frigate sent to drive them away, but more significantly required both seaworthiness and speed to survive on their very demanding stations in all weathers. Berkeley, for example, on the near impossible blockade of Rochefort wrote to Spencer that 'although fast sailing frigates are enabled to work off this shore when caught in a gale at west, it is with the utmost difficulty they can accomplish it' – unless a ship could sail fast in those conditions, it would lose too much ground to leeward to be safe.[82] Of course, frigates had other than fleet duties that influenced their characteristics, but the largest vessels do seem to have been designed with home waters in mind. [83] As a result there was no move to reduce the size of heavy frigates, and 150ft became the norm (even for 36-gun ships for a short while with Henslow's three-ship *Penelope* class of 1797-98).

However, there was one very significant shift in policy – away from dependence on French hull forms. Admiration for French ships never entirely disappeared throughout the war but a reaction did set in based on greater experience of the ships in British service. Those with an understanding of the material consequences of French constructional style had always harboured doubts about their suitability for the Royal Navy and some were not even impressed with their design. Most

continued on page 59

Table 45: *PENELOPE* CLASS 36-GUN FIFTH RATES
Specification

Armament:	Upper deck	Quarterdeck	Forecastle	Guns	Men
Design (4 May 1797)	26 x 18pdrs	6 x 6pdrs, 6 x 32pdr carr	2 x 6pdrs, 2 x 32pdr carr	36	274
Changes by AO: 30 Oct 1798		6pdrs changed to 9pdrs			
20 Feb 1799 (*Jason*)		6 x 9pdrs, 6 x 32pdr carr	4 x 9pdrs, 2 x 32pdr carr		
14 May 1799 (*Amethyst*)		2 x 9pdrs, 10 x 32pdr carr	2 x 9pdrs, 2 x 32pdr carr		
17 Jun 1799 (*Jason*)		2 x 9pdrs, 10 x 32pdr carr	2 x 9pdrs, 4 x 32pdr carr		

Designed by Sir John Henslow

	Lower deck ft-ins	Keel ft-ins	Breadth extreme ft-ins	Depth in hold ft-ins	Burthen tons
Design	150-0	125-5⁷/₈	39-7	13-0	1046
As completed					
Penelope	150-0	125-4¹/₈	39-8¹/₂	13-0	1051
Amethyst	150-0	125-5³/₈	39-7	13-0	1046
Jason	150-2¹/₂	125-5	39-8³/₄	13-0³/₄	1053

Notes:

The ships were designed for 6pdrs although this was clearly an oversight on Henslow's part; the Admiralty reminded him of their order of 25 Apr 1780 that all 38s and 36s were to have 9pdr quarterdeck and forecastle guns and he acknowledged the error.

Armament changes in service are listed in Table 60.

The *Leda* class 38 HMS *Shannon* , contemporary model.

This model, now in the US Naval Academy, was built and presented to Captain Sir Philip Broke after his famous action against the American *Chesapeake* in 1813, so should be an accurate depiction of the *Leda* class as fitted. However, there is no upper deck chase port, and what should be the second quarterdeck carronade port is missing. *(US Naval Academy Museum)*

Table 46: *PENELOPE* CLASS 36-GUN FIFTH RATES
Building Data

Name	Ordered	Builder	Laid down	Launched	Sailed	Fitted at	Fate
Penelope	4 May 1797	Parsons, Bursledon	Jun 1797	26 Sep 1798	30 Nov 1798	Portsmouth	1814 troopship; 1 May 1815 wrecked
Amethyst	4 May 1797	Deptford Dyd	Aug 1798	23 Apr 1799	6 Jun 1799	Deptford	16 Feb 1811 wrecked
Jason	15 Sep 1798	Parsons, Bursledon	Oct 1798	27 Jan 1800	28 May 1800	Portsmouth	21 Jul 1801 wrecked

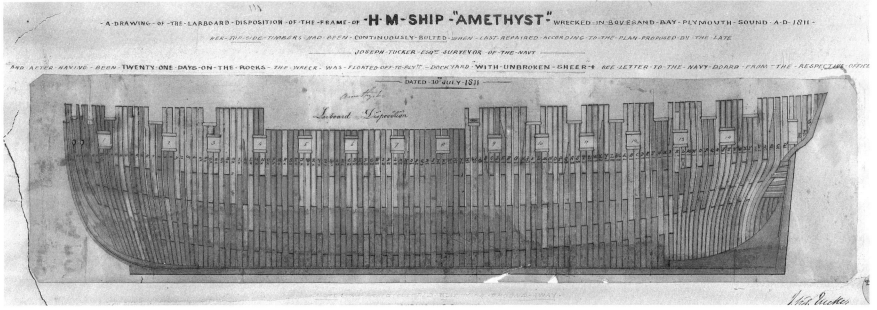

Amethyst, 36 guns, 1797, framing draught, dated 30 July 1811.

The only known plan of this interesting class is this drawing designed to demonstrate the benefits of Joseph Tucker's system of continuously bolting the toptimbers. It shows that the class had a lot of room at either end of the battery, No 1 port being a chase port. *(The Science Museum)*

Table 47: *APOLLO* CLASS 36-GUN FIFTH RATES
Specification

Armament:	Upper deck	Quarterdeck	Forecastle	Guns	Men
Design (15 Nov 1798)	26 x 18pdrs	4 x 9pdrs, 8 x 32pdr carr	4 x 9pdrs, 2 x 32pdr carr	36	264
Changes by AO: 20 Feb 1799		8 x 9pdrs, 4 x 32pdr carr	2 x 9pdrs, 4 x 32pdr carr		
17 Jun 1799		2 x 9pdrs, 10 x 32pdr carr	2 x 9pdrs, 4 x 32pdr carr		
Euryalus (16 Jun 1803)		10 x 32pdr carr	4 x 32pdr carr, 2 x 9pdrs		

Designed by Sir William Rule

	Lower deck ft-ins	Keel ft-ins	Breadth extreme ft-ins	Depth in hold ft-ins	Burthen tons
Design	145-0	121-9³/₈	38-2	13-3	944
As completed					
Apollo	145-0	122-4	38-4	13-3	956
Blanche	145-1	121-9¹/₂	38-3³/₄	13-3	951
Euryalus	145-2	121-11³/₄	38-2¹/₄	13-3	946

Notes:
Because *Apollo* was designed at a period of transition regarding carronades, she was probably subjected to more official changes of mind before entering service than any other frigate.

Armament changes in service are listed in Table 60.

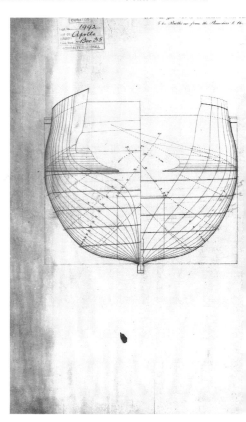

Table 48: *APOLLO* CLASS 36-GUN FIFTH RATES
Building Data

Name	Ordered	Builder	Laid down	Launched	Sailed	Fitted at	Fate
Apollo	15 Sep 1798	Dudman, Deptford	Nov 1798	16 Aug 1799	5 Oct 1799	Deptford	2 Apr 1804 wrecked
Blanche	28 Jan 1800	Dudman, Deptford	Feb 1800	2 Oct 1800	17 Jan 1801	Deptford	19 Jul 1805 captured
Euryalus	16 Aug 1800	Adams, Bucklers Hard	Oct 1801	6 Jun 1803	9 Aug 1803	Portsmouth	1826 prison hulk; 1859 renamed *Africa*; 16 Aug 1860 sold

Note: A further twenty-four (one cancelled) of this class were ordered between 1803 and 1812.

influential of these was Gabriel Snodgrass, the East India Company's equivalent of the Surveyor of the Navy, who published an open letter addressed to Dundas, the Treasurer of the Navy in 1797. In it he stated unequivocally:

> In my opinion, a great deal too much has been said in favour of French ships. I cannot myself see any thing worthy of being copied from them but their magnitude; they are, in other respects, much

Apollo class 36, design sheer draught, dated 14 September 1798.

Although *Apollo* was the prototype of a very large class, only modifications relating to the first two vessels are covered by this draught. By the 1799 establishment they were supposed to carry ten 32pdr carronades and two 9pdrs on the quarterdeck and the enlarged ports in ticked lines relate to this; in fact, there was a shortage of 32pdrs, and it is likely that both went to sea at first with the original design combination of 9pdrs and carronades. Both ships seem to have been completed with the berthed up forecastle.

inferior to British ships of war, being slighter and weaker, in general draw more water, and they likewise commonly exceed the old ships of the present Navy in the absurd tumble-home of their topsides. It must appear very extraordinary, that there are several line-of-battle ships and large frigates now building for Government from draughts copied from these ridiculous ships.[84]

In many respects Snodgrass was ahead of his time (especially his advocacy of wall-sided hulls) but the Admiralty gave a sympathetic hearing to his ideas on fastening ships and he clearly wielded some influence on other aspects of shipbuilding.

However, with many French prizes in service, even some sea officers began to appreciate the problems of French hulls. To individual captains like Byam Martin, the fact that his beloved *Fisgard* was plagued by leaks was little more than a nuisance;[85] but to admirals with strategic responsibilities the absence of a cruiser due to repair or refit could be crucial. By the spring of 1798 Lord Bridport was requesting only

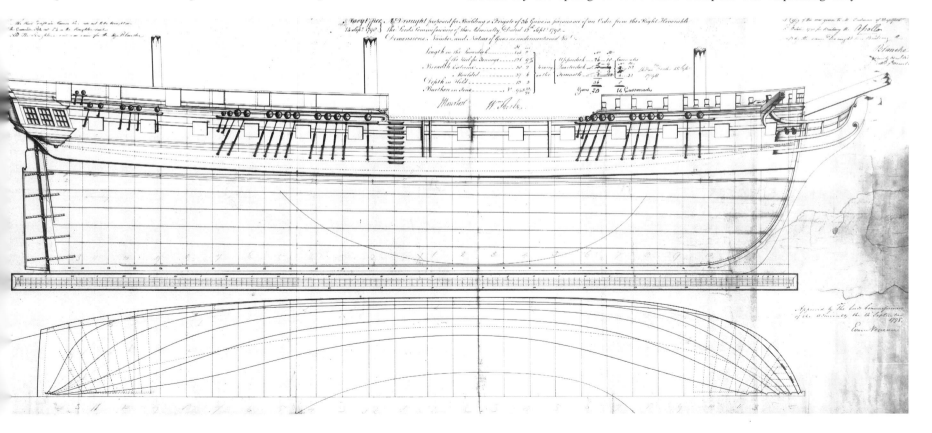

Table 49: *AIGLE* CLASS 36-GUN FIFTH RATES
Specification

Armament:	Upper deck	Quarterdeck	Forecastle	Guns	Men
Design	26 x 18pdrs	4 x 9pdrs,	4 x 9pdrs	36	264
(15 Nov 1798)		8 x 32pdr carr	2 x 32pdr carr		
Changed by AO:					
17 Jun 1799		2 x 9pdrs,	2 x 9pdrs,		
		10 x 32pdr carr	4 x 32pdr carr		
15 Oct 1801		Reversion to Estab of 15 Nov 1798			

Designed by Sir John Henslow

	Lower deck	Keel	Breadth extreme	Depth in hold	Burthen
	ft-ins	ft-ins	ft-ins	ft-ins	tons
Design	146-0	122-1½	38-6	13-0	963
As completed					
Aigle	146-2	122-1	38-8	13-0	971
Resistance	146-1¼	122-1	38-9	13- 0½	975

Armament changes in service are listed in Table 60.

British-built frigates for the Channel Fleet, arguing: 'It is supposed that French frigates sail faster than English built ones. But they are confessedly weaker, are oftener in port and not able to keep the sea on long cruises as they stow little and, having no Orlop Deck, they must move their cables whenever they want to get at the water that is stowed under them.'[86] Opinions like these must have had some effect, and certainly no more French-derived frigate designs were ordered by Lord Spencer's administration.

In some respects, however, French principles continued to dominate: almost every frigate ordered was to a new draught, and British designs grew longer and ever closer to French proportions. The process reached its apogee with the *Penelope* class 36s, the first of their rate which not only added length but actually reduced depth in hold – albeit by only 6in, but enough to give the class the longest and shallowest hull form of any frigate designed by the Surveyors. It is a great misfortune that neither Admiralty draughts nor proper sailing quality reports exist for this intriguing class, but in form they were probably similar to *Active*, reconfigured for thirteen ports, and surviving evidence points to adequate but not outstanding performance under sail.[87] The two of the 1797 programme were joined by one more in 1798 but at the same time there was a reversion to 145-146ft for the next two 36-gun designs, which was the first reversal of the trend towards larger ships since the outbreak of war. This could not reflect dissatisfaction with the actual

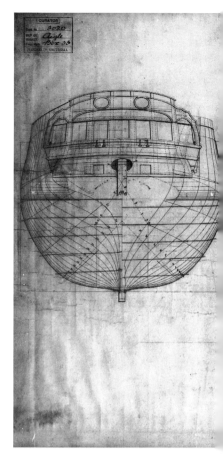

Aigle class 36, design sheer draught, dated 12 November 1798.

These ships seem to have been the first frigates designed from the outset with a solid forecastle barricade. They were subject to a number of alterations during design and construction: the small openings in the barricades to give access to the timberheads were inserted by Admiralty Order of 15 November 1798; the head was raised slightly in both ships, 6 June 1800; and one quarterdeck 9pdr per side was replaced by a 32pdr carronade, requiring the enlargement of No 2 port, 25 November 1800. The draught also includes a later pencil sketch of a circular stern, noted as 'sent to Woolwich, 17 July 1817'.

design of the *Penelope* class since neither ship had even been launched. As explained in the previous chapter, there was to be an even larger 'Admiralty' 36 ordered in 1799, so it could not reflect a major change in Admiralty thinking. It may be that in this case the Surveyors were permitted to indulge their preference for smaller ships.

Henslow's *Aigle* was similar to *Penelope* in the proportion of length to breadth but retained the same depth in hold. She was a good all-round performer under sail, although not quite in the fastest class. Rule's *Apollo* was nearer in proportions to traditional British ratios, and in sailing generally had the edge, particularly in windward performance; when she was new *Apollo* was 'supposed to be one of the fastest ships in the service'.[88] After 1806 this class was adopted as the standard 36 and ordered in considerable numbers; with the exception of a fir-built emergency design of 1812 (itself generally similar to the *Apollo* class),

Table 50: *AIGLE* CLASS 36-GUN FIFTH RATES
Building Data

Name	Ordered	Builder	Laid down	Launched	Sailed	Fitted at	Fate
Aigle	15 Sep 1798	Adams, Bucklers Hard	Nov 1798	23 Sep 1801	6 Oct 1801[1]	Portsmouth	1831 razée 24-gun corvette; 1853 coal hulk; 1869-70 trials ship, BU
Resistance	28 Jan 1800	Parsons, Bursledon	Mar 1800	29 Apr 1801	21 Jun 1801	Portsmouth	31 May 1803 wrecked

Note: [1]Fitted for Ordinary; did not sail until 24 Mar 1803.

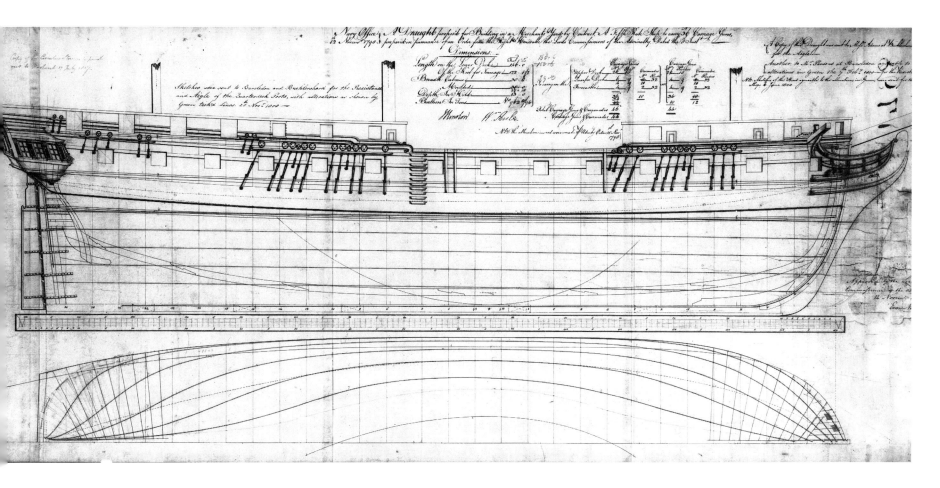

Table 51: *LIVELY* CLASS 38-GUN FIFTH RATE
Specification

Armament:	Upper deck	Quarterdeck	Forecastle	Guns	Men
Design	28 x 18pdrs	2 x 9pdrs, 12 x 32pdr carr	2 x 9pdrs, 2 x 32pdrs carr	38	284

Designed by Sir William Rule

	Lower deck	Keel	Breadth extreme	Depth in hold	Burthen
	ft-ins	ft-ins	ft-ins	ft-ins	tons
Design	154-0	129-8	39-5	13-6	1073
As completed					
Lively	154-1	129-7³/₄	39-6	13-6	1076

Armament changes in service are listed in Table 60.

Table 52: *LIVELY* CLASS 38-GUN FIFTH RATE
Building Data

Name	Ordered	Builder	Laid down	Launched	Sailed	Fitted at	Fate
Lively	15 Oct 1799	Woolwich Dyd	Nov 1801	23 Jul 1804	27 Aug 1804	Woolwich	26 August 1810 wrecked

Note:

Fifteen further vessels of this class were ordered between 1803 and 1812.

they were only 36-gun ships built thereafter. The sailing quality reports suggest that the class fulfilled most, if not all, expectations, but it should be remembered that Henslow retired in 1806 and thereafter only Rule's designs were given serious consideration.

No new 38-gun ship had been designed since 1796 – indeed, only one had been built – but in 1799 a new enlarged class was put in hand. French prizes like *Sybille* and *Minerve* suggested that 154ft on the lower deck was the current norm and Spencer's Admiralty maintained its determination to match French ships in size. The new 38s of the *Lively* class, therefore, adopted this increased length, but for the first time marginally reduced the accepted breadth and depth of the 38, further advancing the move towards French proportions. When originally built they were regarded as different enough to require a bigger complement, but were soon treated as other 38s. They were fine ships, particularly good to

Lively, 38 guns, 1799, pictorial sheer, profile and lines.

The last British frigate design of the eighteenth century was the 154ft *Lively* class 38. These highly successful ships were the culmination of six years' rapid development, marked by increased size, greater length and reduced depth relative to breadth, and a largely carronade secondary armament. This interesting small scale pictorial draught also shows the typical appearance of a frigate of about 1800, with built-up squared-off bulwarks, austere paint scheme, and decorative work reduced to the stem (with a half-length bust figure) and stern areas.

windward and in heavier conditions, although the new British commitment to length meant a loss of manouevrability in these and other classes of this period.

When St Vincent's Board replaced Spencer's early in 1801 there was to be a radical change in policy, with a return to smaller, indigenous, and often antiquated designs, again built in classes of moderate numbers. From 1805 this policy was in turn replaced, after a further brief flirtation with French designs under Barham, by large-scale series construction, but it is significant that of the designs chosen up to 1812, all were in existence in 1800. The larger, faster, and more seaworthy frigates built under the direction of Spencer's Admiralty proved in action that they were more than a match for the best of the French, Spanish or Dutch navies; they also stood the test of time and were a fitting memorial to this most forward-looking of Admiralties.

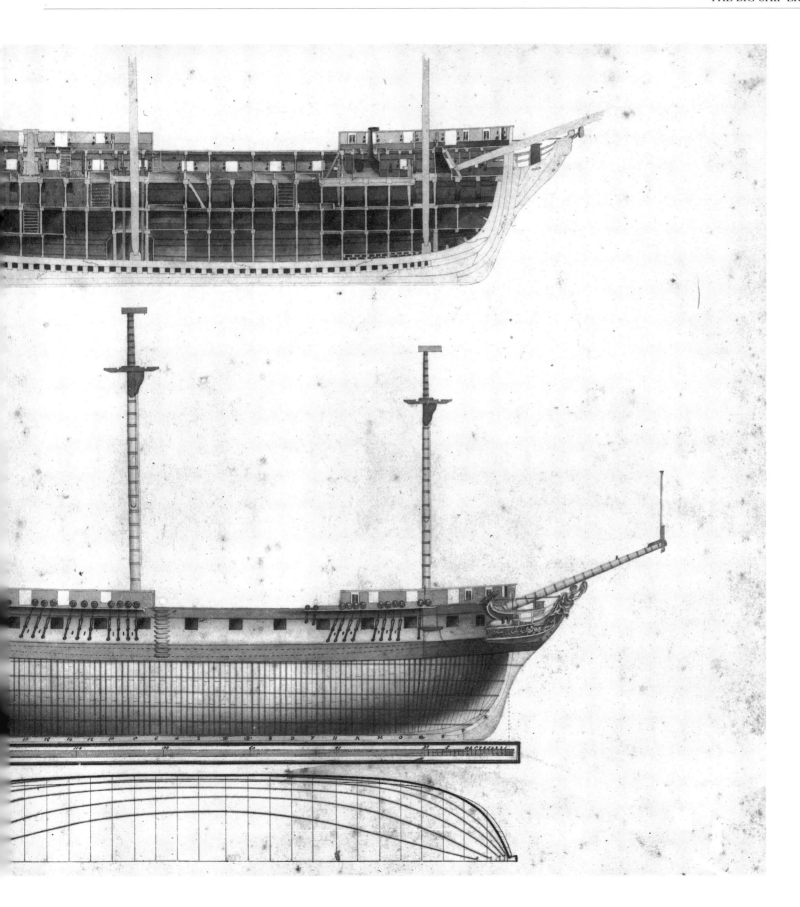

Part II: The Ships

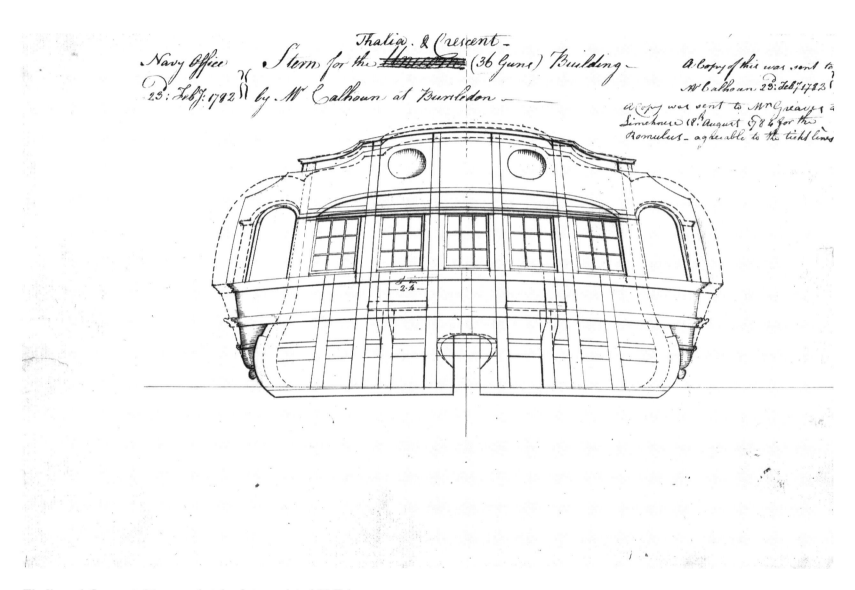

Thalia and *Crescent*, 36 guns, sketch of stern, dated 23 February 1782.

This sketch was sent to Mr Calhoun at Bursledon, a newcomer to frigate-building, introduced during Middleton's time as Comptroller. His work was not entirely satisfactory and in December 1782 he and his partner Nowland were criticised for the quality of their work on the *Thalia*. The sketch also shows, in ticked lines, the new round-topped quarter pieces (for the *Romulus*), a minor appearance change that distinguished the ships of the 1790s from their predecessors.

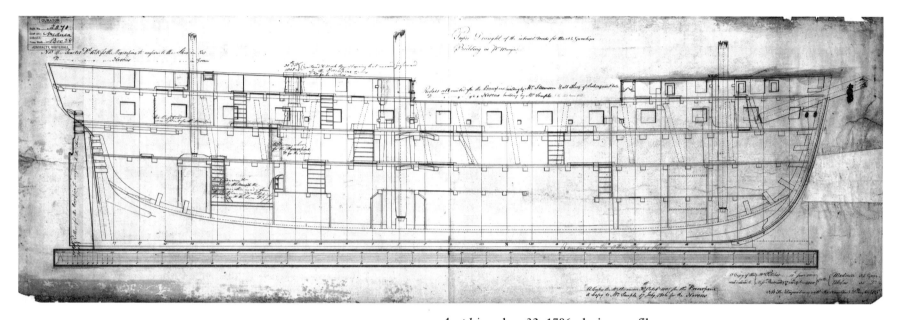

7. Ordering Policy and Shipbuilding

Amphion class 32, 1796, design profile.

This class, the smallest viable 18pdr frigate, was originally designed for a yard with restricted depth of water. After 1800 two more were ordered from builders new to large naval work, where the Admiralty revived the design to minimise its risk by contracting for the smallest useful class.

I n the absence of any systematic recorded discussion of design requirements it might be thought that some indication of Admiralty procurement policy could be reconstructed by an analysis of what rates and classes of ships were actually built. Frigate orders during 1778-83 and 1790-1800 are set out in Tables 53 and 54, and some pattern emerges but it has to be stressed that the Admiralty could not always get either the numbers or the classes it desired.

Probably the major constraint in wartime was shipbuilding capacity, since the Dockyards were far more busy with refits and battle damage repairs and the major commercial builders would have no shortage of customers from the merchant service to replace the usual losses to enemy action. The Navy Board usually patronised the 'River' [*ie* Thames] yards and a few in the Solent area and on the East Coast, all fairly close to London and easy sailing from a major Dockyard where newly launched ships were taken under jury rig for fitting out. In wartime the prices charged by the traditional yards were always subject to inflationary pressure, but they would usually build to government contract if the price was right. At times the Admiralty would not countenance the asking rate, and the ambitious programme of sixteen

frigates proposed in 1795 foundered on this very point. Moreover, even if the price was acceptable, there was a limit to the number of ships the Navy Board could responsibly contract for, given that the usual builders were near enough to the Dockyards to compete for both timber and shipwrights.

During the later stages of the American War an unprecedented programme of new construction was required to meet the overwhelming numbers of the French-Spanish-Dutch alliance, not to mention the Americans or the Armed Neutrality of the North. The Comptroller, Sir Charles Middleton, launched an active search for new builders and his papers include a list of the sites which by his initiative built warships for the first time.[89] The potential problems were: distance, which made it difficult to oversee the work adequately and expensive to bring the ship to a Dockyard; no previous experience with big ships and Navy standards; and lack of suitable facilities and proper capitalisation. On the other hand, it was usually cheaper to build in the 'out ports' than the River.

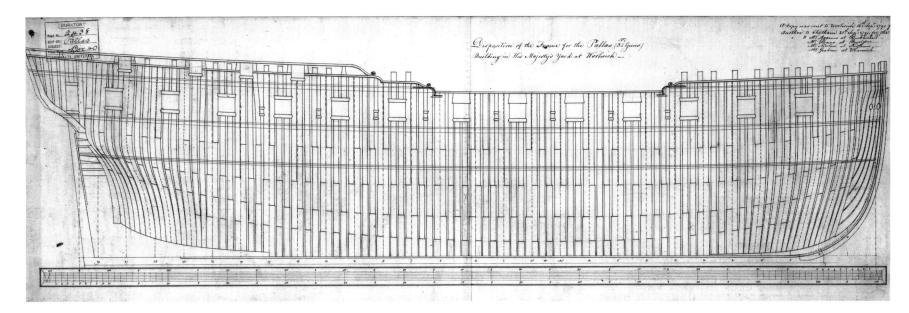

Middleton was aware of the difficulties and sought to contain the risks. In the 1780s he went no further afield than Bristol, and wherever possible introduced the new yards to the Navy's requirements by a sequence of orders rising from small craft like brigs and cutters, via fireships and sloops to frigates. There were few merchant ships of frigate size so for most yards, in modern jargon, the learning curve was a steep one. His programme of 28-gun ships built in the Dover area grew out of an offer from Stewart of Sandgate to build a frigate, after successfully tackling smaller vessels, but although the Admiralty did not want frigates of less than 32 guns,[90] 28-gun ships were the largest the Navy Board felt could be built safely on the open beach site, so the class was re-introduced.

An overseer was appointed from among the Shipwrights of the nearest Royal Dockyard for each ship under construction in a merchant yard, so there was some check on quality of build, although he was not in permanent residence. Examples of intentionally skimped work created too much scandal to be common,[91] but lack of experience with Navy standards and practices did provoke some dissatisfaction with some of the new builders. For example, the *Thalia*, 36 guns was subjected to a rigorous inspection in December 1782 and Calhoun & Nowland were censured for the inadequate number of trenails and the rough quality of finish. The Navy Board undoubtedly regarded the time and effort involved as worthwhile in the long run since it expanded the total number of builders with naval experience. When Middleton went to the Admiralty as Lord Barham in 1805 he adopted a similar strategy, introducing a number of yards to frigate-building with orders for 18pdr 32-gun ships; by that time they were the smallest viable frigates and the class seems to have been revived entirely for this purpose.

Most of the new builders were small and poorly capitalised so there was always a risk of their becoming financially overstretched by being encouraged to take on contracts for far larger vessels than previously.

continued on page 70

Pallas class 32, 1791, design framing draught.

This class was ordered in 1790, not in response to the threat of war with Spain as might be expected, but to use up timber of relatively small scantling lying idle in the Royal Dockyards. The framing scheme shows no major developments over those of the 1780s, but a curved bearding line has replaced a stepped line in the after cants.

Euryalus (*Apollo*) class 36, design sheer draught, dated 18 August 1800.

One of the few areas of wooden shipbuilding where there was a distinct labour-saving advantage in repeating a design was in the 'lofting' – the transfer of shapes from a scale plan to full size timbers, which involved making accurate moulds. These were time-consuming to construct but could be reused, and a number of builders offered better terms if they could contract for repeat designs. However, the economic benefits of mass-production that industrial processes can achieve were not available: the large numbers of ships built to this draught reflect general satisfaction with the design, combined with the post-Trafalgar strategic view that only large numbers of ships would win the war, but there were no dramatic economies of scale in building to one draught.

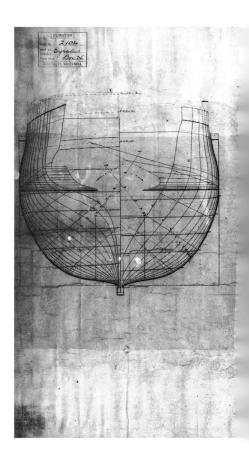

Table 53: THE PATTERN OF FRIGATE ORDERS 1778-1782

DATE ORDERED		28-GUN SHIPS Name	Designer	32-GUN SHIPS Name	Designer	36-GUN SHIPS Name	Designer	38-GUN SHIPS Name	Designer
	1778			4 Amazons	Williams				
				5 Actives	Hunt				
5 Nov	1778					Flora	Williams	Minerva	Hunt
12 Feb	1779							Arethusa	Hunt
12 Mar	1779							Latona	Williams
	1779			2 Amazons	Williams				
				2 Actives	Hunt				
9 Sep	1779			Quebec					
3 Dec	1779					Perseverance	Hunt		
1 Feb	1780			Andromache	Williams				
1 Mar	1780							Phaeton	Hunt
20 Mar	1780			Hermione	Hunt				
				Druid	Hunt				
19 Dec	1780					Unicorn	Williams		
3 Jan	1781			Syren	Williams				
20 Jan	1781			Andromeda	Hunt				
10 May	1781			Heroine	[Purchased]				
2 Jun	1781					Phoenix	Hunt		
11 Aug	1781					Crescent	Williams		
7 Sep	1781			Penelope	Hunt				
22 Sep	1781							Thetis	Hunt
5 Oct	1781			Iris	Williams				
22 Oct	1781			Greyhound	Williams				
8 Dec	1781					Inconstant	Hunt		

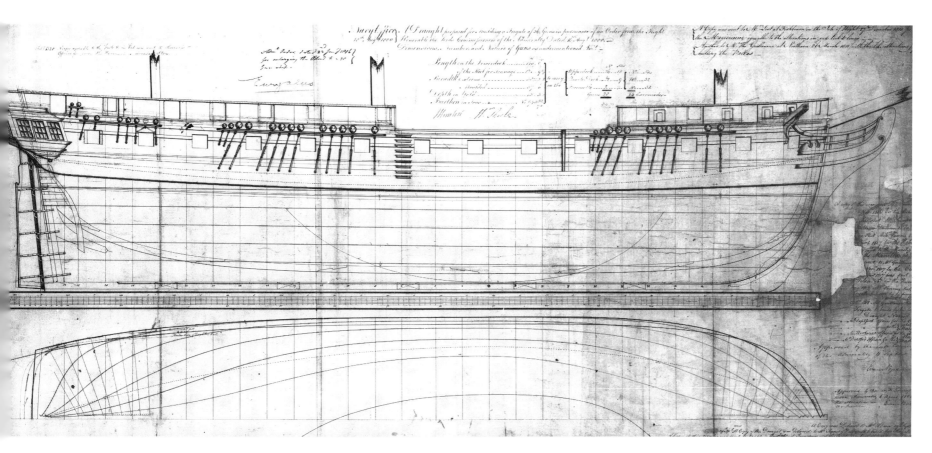

Table 53: THE PATTERN OF FRIGATE ORDERS 1778-1782 (continued)

DATE ORDERED		28-GUN SHIPS Name	Designer	32-GUN SHIPS Name	Designer	36-GUN SHIPS Name	Designer	38-GUN SHIPS Name	Designer
28 Dec	1781					Romulus	Williams		
11 Jan	1782			Meleager	Williams				
14 Jan	1782					Cassandra [canc 21 Mar 1782]	'lines of *Prudente*'		
30 Jan	1782			Castor	Williams				
23 Feb	1782	Thisbe	Williams						
6 Mar	1782	Circe	Williams						
15 Mar	1782	Rose	Williams						
22 Mar	1782					Leda	Hunt		
26 Mar	1782	Hussar	Williams						
17 Apr	1782							Melampus	Hunt
23 Apr	1782			Aquilon	Hunt				
7 May	1781	Alligator	Williams						
5 Jun	1782	Dido	Williams						
23 Jul	1782			Solebay	Williams				
29 Jul	1782			Terpsichore	Williams				
9 Aug	1782			Blanche	Hunt				
20 Aug	1782			Blonde	Williams				
2 Oct	1782	Hind	Slade						
22 Oct	1782	Lapwing	Williams						
		Laurel [canc 7 Oct 1783]	Slade						

Note: The 28s and 32s are included to give an idea of the sequence and balance of numbers of the 18pdr ships compared with smaller cruisers. It is also an opportunity to print the order dates for 28s and 32s that are not in the Progress Books and consequently omitted from the author's previous book *The First Frigates*.

Table 54: THE PATTERN OF FRIGATE ORDERS 1790-1800

DATE ORDERED	32-GUN SHIPS Name	Designer	36-GUN SHIPS Name	Designer	38-GUN SHIPS Name	Designer	LARGER Name	Designer
9 Dec 1790	**Pallas Class** Pallas Stag Unicorn	Henslow						
14 Feb 1793	**Improved *Pallas* Class** Alcmene Galatea Lively Cerberus	Henslow			**Artois Class** Artois Diana Diamond Apollo Jason Seahorse	Henslow		
25 May 1794			**Inconstant Lengthened** Phoebe Caroline Dryad Doris	Henslow				
			Amazon Class Amazon Emerald	Rule				
6 Nov 1794					[Active][1] [Amazon][1] [Leda][1]			
4 Feb 1795	**Fir-built *Alcmene* Class** Maidstone Shannon	Henslow	**Fir-built *Amazon* Class** Trent Tweed	Rule	**Fir-built *Artois* Class** Tamer Clyde	Henslow		

Table 54: THE PATTERN OF FRIGATE ORDERS 1790-1800 (continued)

DATE ORDERED	32-GUN SHIPS Name	Designer	36-GUN SHIPS Name	Designer	38-GUN SHIPS Name	Designer	LARGER Name	Designer
30 Apr 1795			**Lines of *San Fiorenzo*** *Sirius*		**Artois Class** *Ethalion*	Henslow	**Cambrian Class** *Cambrian*	Henslow
					Naiad Class *Naiad*	Rule	**Acasta Class** *Acasta*	Rule
					Lines of *Impérieuse* *Boadicea*		**Lines of *Pomone*** *Endymion*	
					Lines of *Melpomène* *Hydra*			
7 Apr 1796	**Triton Class** *Triton*	'Admiralty'						
27 Apr 1796					**Improved *Artois* Class** *Active*	Henslow		
					Amazon Class *Amazon*	Rule		
					Lines of the *Hebe* *Leda*			
11 Jun 1796	**Amphion Class** *Amphion*	Rule						
16 Dec 1796							**Lavinia Class** *Lavinia*	Barrallier
15 Feb 1797					**Amazon Class** *Hussar*	Rule		
4 May 1797			**Penelope Class** *Penelope* *Amethyst*	Henslow				
13 Jan 1798	**Narcissus Class** *Narcissus*	Henslow						
15 Sep 1797			**Apollo Class** *Apollo*	Rule				
			Aigle Class *Aigle*	Henslow				
			'As *Penelope*' *Jason*	Rule				
7 Sep 1799			**Ethalion Class** *Ethalion*	'Admiralty'				
15 Oct 1799					**Lively Class** *Lively*	Rule		
28 Jan 1800	**Amphion Class** *Medusa* *Aeolus*	Rule	**Phoebe Class** *Fortunee*	Henslow				
			Apollo Class *Blanche*	Rule				
	Narcissus Class *Tartar*	Henslow						
			Aigle Class *Resistance*	Henslow				
16 Aug 1800			**Apollo Class** *Euryalus*	Rule				

Notes:
[1]This order for three 38s was rescinded, and not reinstated until 27 April 1796.

The Navy Board advanced money at set stages in the construction process, but the management of a cashflow with short peaks and long troughs was too much for some yards, who were forced out of business. The Navy Board was careful in its assessment of each builder's capacity and before 1800 the number of ships completely lost by business failure was low, although a few had to be completed by other builders or transferred to Royal Dockyards.[92] After 1800 the Navy Board was pressurised by St Vincent's Admiralty to avoid their traditional suppliers and by subsequent administrations to find additional sources. The Navy Board, like any purchasing agency, knew that the relationship with a supplier was a subtle one and had to be mutually beneficial. Therefore it objected to the Admiralty's attempts to impose onerous conditions on the merchants and particularly opposed an order of 1806 telling them always to take the lowest tender, pointing out that 'the needy adventurer, whose means are inadequate to the fulfilling his engagements... is the most likely to offer the lowest terms'.[93] Such was the need for additional construction, however, that some unsound builders received contracts; not surprisingly, the number of ships affected by bankruptcy increased.[94]

Even if he had the experience and the resources to build a frigate, not every merchant builder had an ideal site. Anybody who has visited the old Bucklers Hard yard at Beaulieu (which built 74s) can see how little water was needed, but even this was not always available. This left the Admiralty with the dilemma of not fully exploiting capacity or building smaller ships than ideally required. This latter was adopted when the need was pressing, and the 18pdr 32s of the *Amphion* class were originally designed to fit the Betts yard at Mistleythorn, and the *Narcissus* for the basin at Deptford Dockyard that had a narrow access to the Thames. On the other hand, Barham's programme of 32s mentioned earlier, was primarily an apprenticeship in frigate-building for new merchant yards, since restricted water cannot have been a problem in the Humber and Tyne where they were built. However, the Navy Board did turn down an offer from the Frindsbury shipbuilder Brindley to build one of them at his Kings Lynn yard because they felt the river was unsuitable.[95]

The search for new capacity had some curious ramifications. The failure of Jacobs, the builder at Milford Haven, left the 74 *Milford* and the big frigate *Lavinia* to be completed by the government; because there was no Dockyard close by this had to be *in situ*, and from this small beginning the Pembroke Dockyard was to develop. External sources were also considered and Samuel Bentham, the ingenious Inspector-General of Naval Works, was sent to explore the possibilities of shipbuilding in Russia; for a while in 1805 there were high hopes of building two 74s and two 36-gun frigates at Kronstadt. St Vincent had looked even further afield, at Bermuda and Bombay, and although only small craft were built at the former, India became a source of a limited number of battleships and frigates built of Malabar teak.

Besides looking for extra capacity the Admiralty also sought to make more efficient use of what was regularly available. Slips were occupied while ships stood in frame to season and at times of extreme emergency

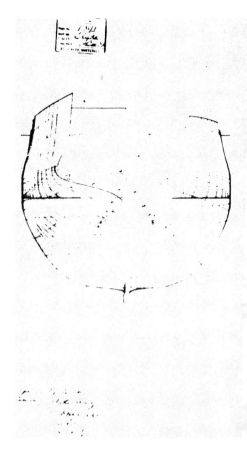

Clyde (fir-built *Artois*) class 38, design sheer draught, dated 2 February 1795.

Building fir ships was both a reponse to the general shortage of timber and to the shortage of ships, since they could be put together very quickly in periods of special need. At times the paucity of specific types of timber, particularly 'grown' pieces for knees, became acute, and in 1804 led to a unique revival of the old practice of rebuilding. *Clyde* was reconstructed to the same draught, saving the iron and wooden knees, floor timbers, iron stanchions, masts, yards and furniture of the dismantled hull. The 'rebuild' was also called *Clyde*, but she was in every important respect a new ship.

frigates were ordered to be launched without even the minimum six months' standing time. There were standard penalties for late delivery, but occasionally positive financial incentives were tried to speed up construction.[96] In the Dockyards, more emphasis was placed on planning and the practice grew up in the 1790s of ordering ships before a slip was free. This allowed the Dockyard to begin work on converting and seasoning timber in advance, saving space (unconverted timber was more bulky) and time, since large amounts of the frame already existed by the time the ship was laid down, and might even reduce seasoning time in frame. Thought was also given to economies of scale: the moulds could be reused for ships of the same design and in 1797 the order for a 36 was changed to a 38 at the request of Woolwich Dockyard which was already building one of the same class. While Spencer's Admiralty built many small groups and one-off designs there was not much scope for this approach, but it was more widely adopted in the following war, when even merchant builders petitioned for repeat orders of specific designs.[97] This could have a warping effect on ordering policy, as in the case of the *Orlando*, one of St Vincent's repeats of the *Inconstant* class, which was ordered at Chatham Dockyard's suggestion in 1808 to reuse the moulds. Three years earlier, what should have been the last of the class was cancelled because this small ship did not make the maximum use of the available slip!

Before 1800 logistical constraints were noticeable but not crucial, whereas growing shortages, particularly of seasoned compass timber,

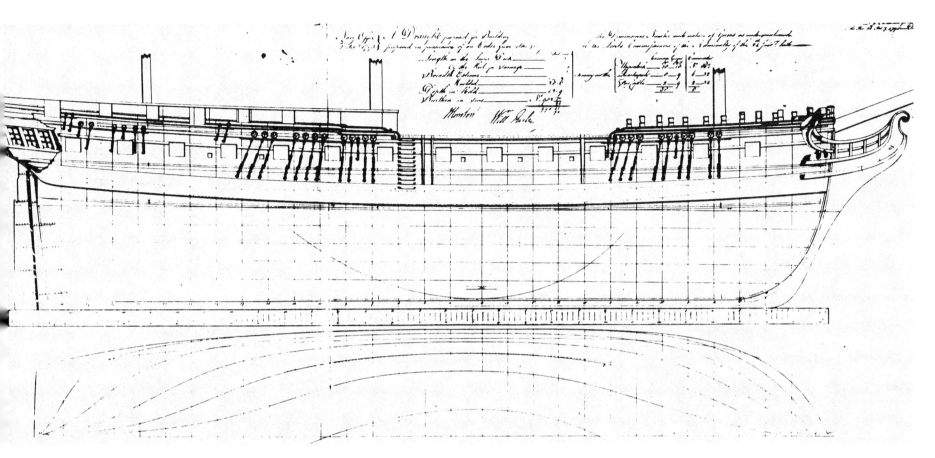

were to further compromise the Admiralty's frigate programmes later. It is anticipating the next volume somewhat, but to underline the contrast, it seems fair to say that the emphasis in the 1793-1800 period was on improving design, but after 1801 it was on increasing numbers. New design was almost entirely abandoned in favour of large scale construction of established successful classes, and every opportunity was taken to conserve timber. The unique rebuilding of the fir *Clyde* in 1804 has been mentioned in an earlier chapter, and the *Thames*, a small 12pdr 32 building at the same time, employed much scavenged timber from vessels broken up.[98] Perhaps an even more telling example is the 1809 order for the *Surprise* at Milford – placed purely to use as much as possible of the serviceable remains of the *Leda*, which was wrecked locally the previous year.[99]

'Inboard works Expanded for a 38 Gun ship', dated Deptford, 14 May 1808.

'Outside Plank Expanded for a 38 Gun ship', dated Deptford, 14 May 1808.

Planking expansions are rare at this period, and these have been catalogued as the *Diana* of 1794. However, in his monograph on the ship David White says they do not depict the actual state of any ship of the class. They are certainly mysterious, since the annotation attributes them to no specific class; on the other hand, they have no bridle port, which for 38-gun ships strongly suggests the *Artois* class. The berthed up forecastle indicates a later date, and the mixed long gun/carronade ports could be right for the 1805-6 period when there was a short-lived attempt to make non-recoil carronades standard, but in any event there is one port too few in the quarterdeck bulwark. The drawings were probably intended to illustrate general principles, rather than a specific class, and they do show where anchor-stock and top-and-butt planking were employed, as well as the general shift of butts.

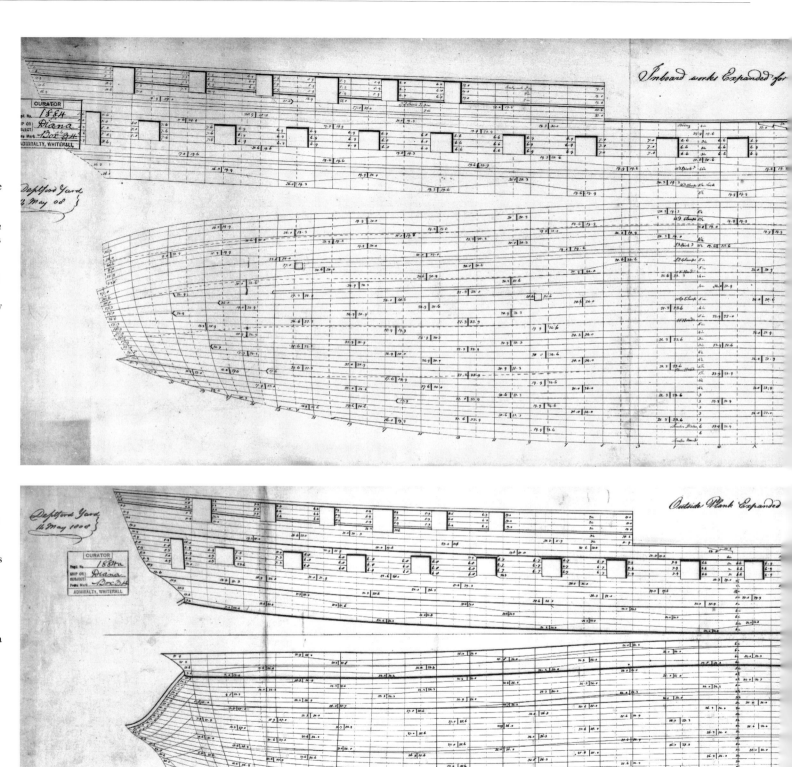

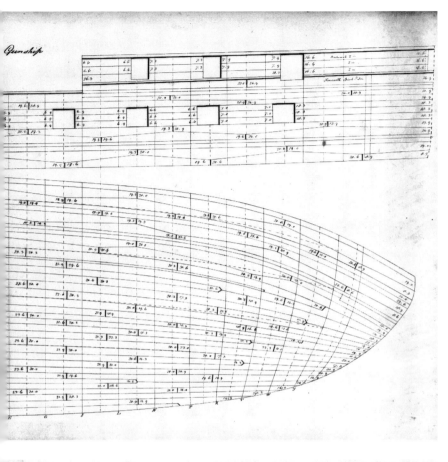

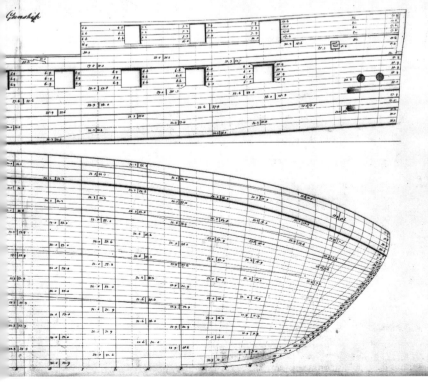

8. Design

The 18pdr frigate was introduced at a period of relative conservatism in British design and the first 38s and 36s had the characteristically short, deep hulls of the period. This tended to make them manoeuvrable and good sea-boats, although the latter characteristic was compromised by carrying the gun battery so near the ends of the hull that heavy pitching was a consequence. However, they were not particularly fast in light winds, even if a good reserve of stability meant that they could carry more canvas in heavier conditions. They also tended to be weatherly, which could offset the lack of pure speed when in chase.

The decade after 1790 was to see a radical change in British frigate design, characterised by a threefold move away from traditional policy:

1. A rapid increase in absolute size

2. Frequent design changes, many 'one-off' ships and experimental hull forms

3. A significant shift in proportions, towards longer hulls. These developments are summarised in Table 55, from which data the underlying trends can be extrapolated.

The 'French influence' of this period is self-evident in ships like *Boadicea*, *Hydra* and *Sirius* which employed the dimensions and hull forms of prizes, but it also underlies the move away from large numbers built to the same draught. Traditionally, French ships were designed in the arsenals by different constructors to a common specification, producing a variety of individual ships,[100] and Lord Spencer's Admiralty seems to have been attempting to achieve a similar result.[101] Less obvious but equally significant is the distinct progression towards French proportions, and since the 'Admiralty' experiments are the most extreme examples it seems certain that the Naval Lords rather than the Surveyors were the driving force.

However, the Surveyors in many ways were the guardians of traditional British virtues in ship design and it is worth noting that the one dimension they were most reluctant to reduce was depth in hold. In absolute terms French frigates might have had anything up to 2ft less, which as pointed out in earlier chapters made their orlops and storage spaces too cramped for the long range cruising requirements of the Royal Navy. In general, the alterations to British frigate forms came about by adding length (and to a much lesser extent, breadth) to a virtually fixed depth in hold: 13ft 9in for 38s, about 13ft 4in for 36s, and 12ft 6in for 32s.

In this context the albeit small reductions in depth in the *Penelope* class 36s of 1797 and the *Lively* class 38s of 1799 mark a precedent, and probably indicate the victory of the Naval Lords' views over those of the Surveyors. Not surprisingly, in relative terms *Triton* is the shallowest and *Ethalion* the longest frigate of the period, and both have rather less

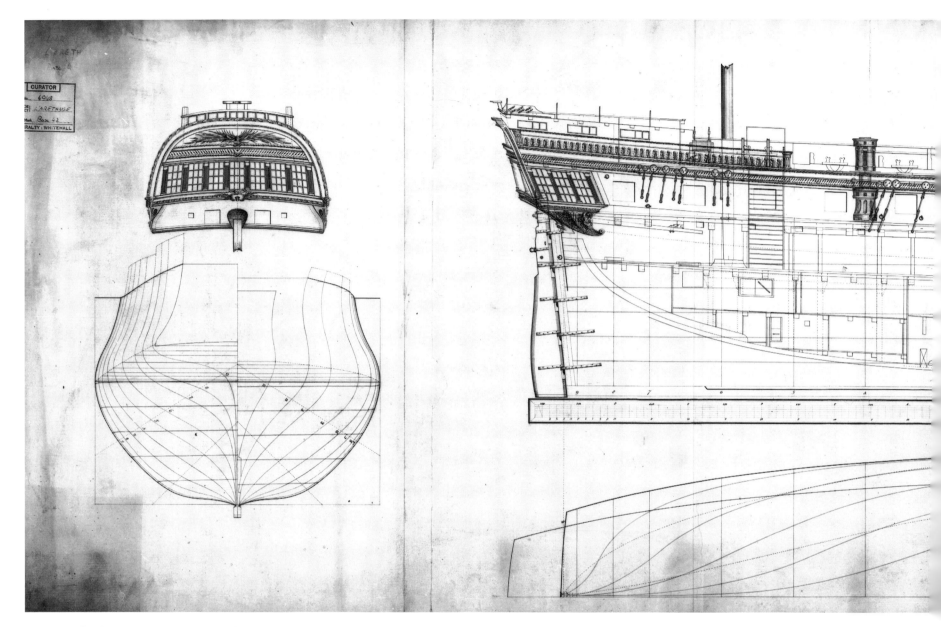

Aréthuse, 38 guns, ex-French, sheer & profile as taken off at Sheerness, April 1795.

This ship is a good example of French design principles. With hull ratios of 3.83 (length:breadth), 3.22 (breadth:depth) and 12.33 (length:depth), she was not the most extreme French frigate in her proportions, but while some British frigates matched her L:B ratio, none was as shallow. The lack of space below the lower deck was a constant source of complaint about French frigates in Royal Navy service. An odd feature of this particular ship was the lightness of the works above the gunwale – virtually nothing on the forecastle, and the flimsiest of rails on the quarterdeck. This was presumably intended to cut down windage, but this emphasis seems compromised by the erection of the *demi-dunette* or small cabin on the quarterdeck. These structures commonly provided an office and/or bedplace for the captain, but the practice died out during the Revolutionary War under pressure to find space for more guns or carronades.

depth in hold than standard for their rate. The alterations to the *Amphion* class, coming hot on the heels of the *Triton* order should also be remembered: not only is the raked bow and very flat sheer reminiscent of Gambier's design, but the extra length ordered gave the *Amphion* more 'French' proportions than any of the Surveyors' previous frigates. Gambier is sometimes credited with the 'design' of Rule's first battleship, the *Plantagenet*,[102] and it may be that his involvement in this class was similar: something close to a collaboration for which Rule retained the principal credit. Henslow, the senior Surveyor, was known to oppose the increases in size ordered at this period and was regarded by later Admiralties as a major obstacle to improvement,[103] but Rule may have been more susceptible to ideas from the senior Board – at least in his younger days when junior Surveyor.

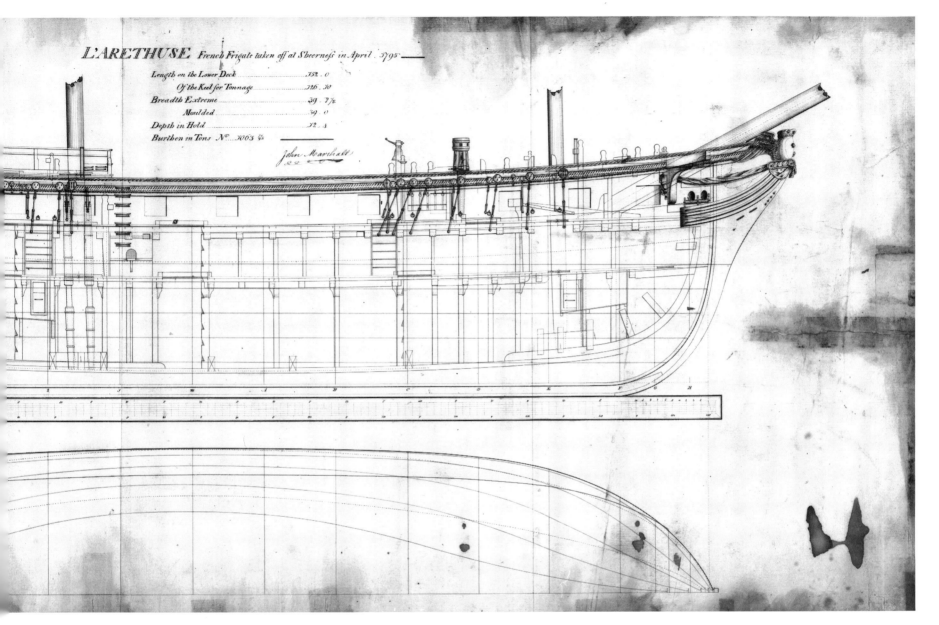

L'ARETHUSE French Frigate taken off at Sheerness in April 1795

Length on the Lower Deck	152 . 0
Of the Keel for Tonnage	126 . 10
Breadth Extreme	39 . 7½
Moulded	39 . 0
Depth in Hold	12 . 4
Burthen in Tons Nᵒ. 1003 ⁴⁄

John Marshall

Accepting that the increase in size was largely a matter of length, the way that it was utilised also shows a certain consistency. Usually the extra length was applied at the ends of the battery (and not between the guns), which in theory allowed finer lines fore and aft for greater speed, or at least offered a reduced tendency to pitching. A distance of 6½ft between ports was deemed satisfactory for most classes down to 1795, although the first 36s contrived 7ft. Significantly, the *Melampus* design kept the tighter spacing of the 38s when altered to a 36, and the first attempts to increase the distance between guns were both considered failures - to 7ft in the 148ft 38-gun *Naiad*, and to 7½ft in the 142ft 36s of the *Phoebe* class. It is possible that the increases in length were driven by the desire to have more space between the guns and the advantages of finer ends; certainly the ensuing classes settled down to 7ft between

ports for all 18pdr frigates, the minimum practical length being 150ft for fourteen-port ships and 144-145ft for those with thirteen.

A minor feature associated with this development is the regular adoption of the bridle port. As its name suggests, it was originally used for handling the mooring bridles, but it came to be seen as a main deck chase port.[104] When the No 1 port was right forward on what the seventeenth century called the luff of the bow, it had some use for a chase gun, but when moved aft a separate port was required. This was a common feature in the French navy, even before its formal adoption in April 1787,[105] but its exact status is ambiguous. Few French frigates seem to have been designed with fourteen gunports plus a bridle (and those, like *Didon, Uranie, Aréthuse, Révolutionnaire* and *Seine*, were built in the years immediately following the 1787 ordinance). Judging from

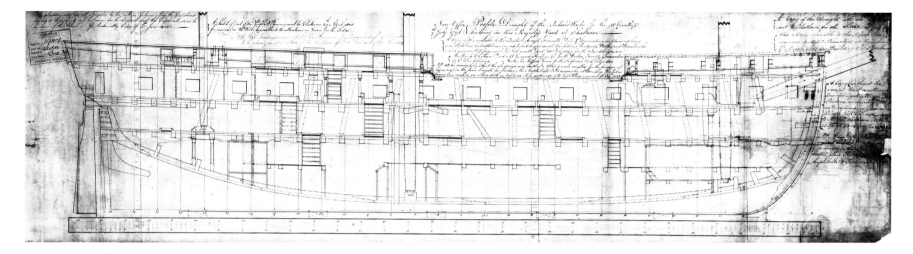

Leda class 38, design profile draught, dated 9 July 1796.

The adoption of French hull forms meant compromise in the internal layout. This much-used *Leda* class draught shows that a forward magazine could not be contrived under the fore platform, but had to be inserted in a hanging position, taking up space normally occupied by a sail room, stores, etc.

relative position and spacing, many nominal French 40s seem to have had thirteen gunports plus a bridle, with the latter armed permanently. This is true of the 1795 ships based on French models, which therefore did not include a proper port.

In British service, bridle ports were common in the 1760s, but neglected in the ships of the Williams/Hunt generation, only to be revived in some captured frigates during the major repairs carried out in response to the 1790 war scare. However, after the French war broke out the matter was given greater priority. The captain of the new 38 *Artois* had requested one in January 1794,[106] and although it was declined on the grounds of the problems of cutting a chase port in a ship designed without one, it obviously led to consideration of their utility. The *Naiad* draught was altered to incorporate one, and later ships were designed with one from the outset; *Fortunee*, a late addition to the *Phoebe* class, involved some considerable redesign of the head to include one, so they had obviously been accepted as essential by 1800.

By way of conclusion, it should be pointed out that the frigates of the 1790s were generally approved, even by the most censorious of judges, their officers. The line of battleships continued to cause unease in some respects, but frigate design was far less controversial. An article in the *Naval Chronicle* in 1803, otherwise critical of British warships, opined: 'Our frigates in general sail well, and are sufficiently stiff; those of thirty-six and thirty-eight guns are admirable ships.'[107] On an official level, when the new Barham Admiralty requested draughts of existing 38s and 32s 'of approved character in the service', the Navy Board was spoilt for choice.[108] It was widely believed that there had been a substantial improvement in the general standards of performance, to the point where there was not much to choose between classes. To the more thoughtful, this suggested that the precise form of the hull was less important than more general factors like its proportions and, especially, its size in relation to the weight of metal carried.[109] Snodgrass' view that it was only the size of French ships that made them superior came to be more widely accepted and after 1800 the 'French influence' was on the wane. Curiously, the head of the Admiralty which so whole-heartedly embraced the myth of French superiority was himself a complete sceptic: in a letter to Sidney Smith, Lord Spencer described how on the subject of French prizes the 'opinion, or rather fancies' of his naval advisers always suggested 'the last we take is the best possible'; to Spencer it was no more than a 'fashion'.[110]

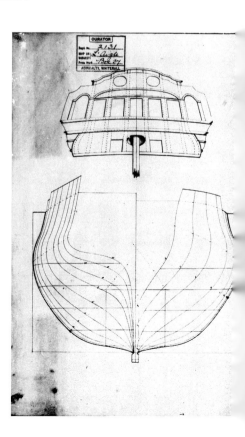

Aigle, 38 guns, ex-French (captured 1782), sheer & profile as repaired, July 1790.

This ship was one of the frigates to undergo major repairs as part of the 'Spanish Armament' of 1790. The ship has been given the topside detail, fittings and internal layout of a standard British 18pdr frigate but, interestingly, also a bridle port; this is one of the first examples of the revived employment of a chase port, which was to become *de rigueur* for British frigates from the mid-1790s.

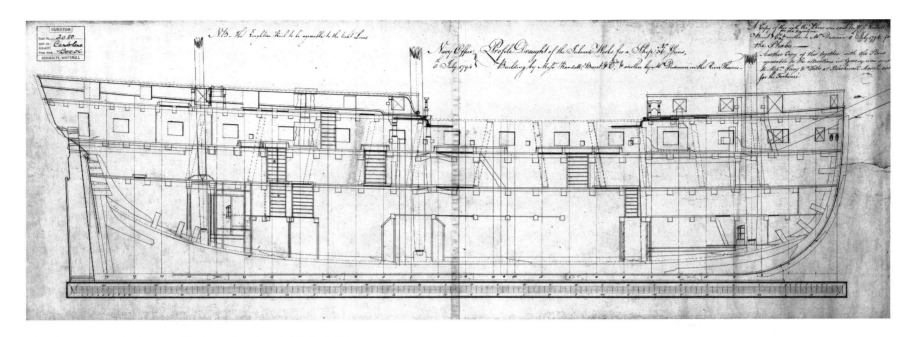

Phoebe class 36, design profile draught, dated 8 July 1794.

The bridle, or fore chase, port came to be considered essential in a very short space of time in the mid-1790s. When a late addition to the *Phoebe* class, the *Fortunee*, was ordered in 1800, the design was modified as shown on this draught to move the foremost gunport aft and add a chase port. Also representative of 1790s development are the modified solid barricades for forecastle and quarterdeck, with their additional gunports.

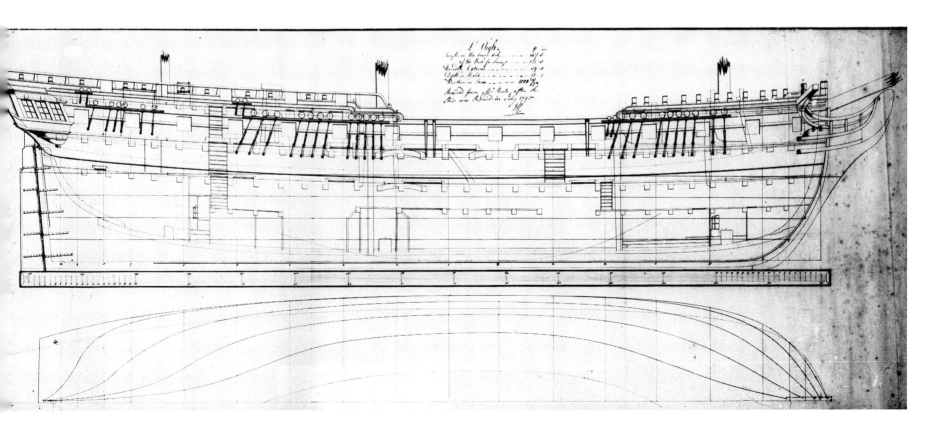

Table 55: PROPORTIONS OF 18pdr FRIGATES 1778-1800

Dimensions (feet): Ratios:	Length	L:B	Breadth	B:D	Depth	L:D
BRITISH CLASSES						
1778						
Minerva, 38	141.0	3.63	38.83	2.82	13.75	10.25
1779						
Perseverance, 36	137.0	3.61	38.0	2.83	13.42	10.21
1790						
Beaulieu, 40	147.25	3.73	39.5	2.60	15.22	9.67
Pallas, 32	135.0	3.75	36.0	2.88	12.5	10.8
1793						
Alcmene, 32	135.0	3.70	36.5	2.92	12.5	10.8
Artois, 38	146.0	3.74	39.0	2.84	13.75	10.62
1794						
Phoebe, 36	142.5	3.75	38.0	2.81	13.42	10.55
Amazon, 36	143.0	3.75	38.16	2.83	13.5	10.51
1795						
Naiad, 38	147.0	3.73	39.42	2.87	13.75	10.69
Boadicea, 38	148.5	3.74	39.66	3.13	12.66	11.64
Hydra, 38	148.16	3.76	39.33	3.11	12.66	11.70
Sirius, 36	148.83	3.96	39.58	2.99	13.25	11.23
1796						
Triton, 32	142.0	3.94	36.0	3.04	11.23	12.00
Active, 38	150.0	3.77	39.75	2.89	13.75	10.91
Amazon, 38	150.0	3.81	39.42	2.87	13.75	10.91
Leda, 38	150.13	3.76	39.92	3.13	12.75	11.77
Amphion, 32	144.0	3.84	37.5	3.00	12.5	11.52
1797						
Penelope, 36	150.0	3.80	39.5	3.04	13.0	11.54
1798						
Narcissus, 32	142.0	3.79	37.5	3.00	12.5	11.36
Apollo, 36	145.0	3.80	38.16	2.88	13.25	10.94
Aigle, 36	146.0	3.79	38.5	2.96	13.0	11.23
1799						
Ethalion, 36	152.0	4.00	38.0	2.92	13.0	11.69
Lively, 38	154.0	3.91	39.42	2.92	13.5	11.41
FRENCH SHIPS						
1782						
Junon, 38	148.83	3.78	39.38	3.07	12.83	11.60
1785						
Proserpine, 40	151.33	3.81	39.74	3.17	12.54	12.07
1788						
Tartu, 40	154.42	3.85	40.15	3.09	13.0	11.88
1790						
Perle, 40	150.33	3.81	39.42	3.06	12.88	11.67
1791						
Aréthuse, 40	152.0	3.83	39.71	3.22	12.33	12.33
Sybille, 44	154.25	3.84	40.13	3.25	12.33	12.51
1793						
Seine, 40	156.75	3.87	40.5	3.27	12.38	12.66
Résistance, 40	160.5	3.94	40.71	3.06	13.29	12.08
1794						
Minerve, 40	154.38	3.87	39.92	3.07	13.0	11.88
1795						
Immortalité, 38	145.17	3.71	39.17	3.43	11.42	12.71
1796						
Diane, 40	155.83	3.83	40.71	3.24	12.58	12.39
1798						
Africaine, 40	153.83	3.85	39.92	3.19	12.5	12.31
1800						
Pallas, 38	146.66	3.70	39.63	3.30	12.0	12.22

Note: The British classes are arranged by order date. The French ships are a selection from the prize lists, arranged by date of building.

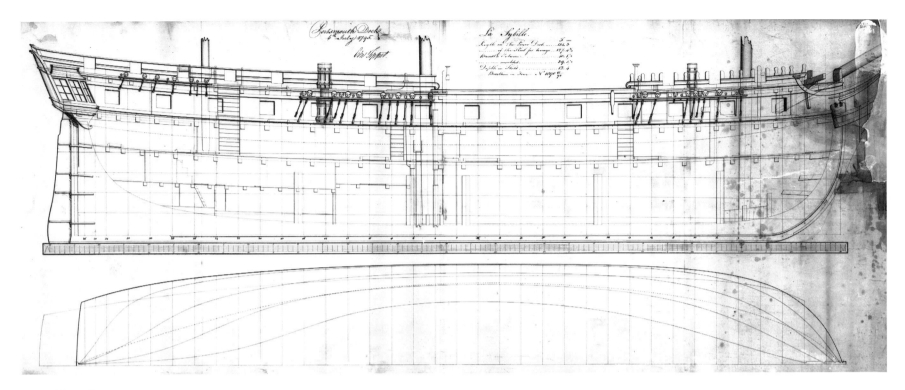

9: Performance

Even at the time, it was recognised that the 1790s was a period of general improvement in the performance of British frigates. Whereas the best classes had been capable of about 13kts under optimum conditions during the 1760s, in the American War despite the widespread adoption of copper sheathing 12kts was rarely achieved and 11kts nearer the norm. The 18pdr cruiser had been introduced during the latter period, and the 36s in particular were not very fast; the 38s were better, but there was a widely held belief that French frigates were superior under sail.

The frigate designs of the 1790s were part of a conscious attempt to raise standards in Britain. Not only were the ships larger in absolute terms (which will tend to greater speed), but they were also relatively longer. In a navy that enjoyed the overwhelming superiority of the British in the 1790s, where so much of its cruising experience was in chase of a reluctant enemy, it is not surprising that speed became a much sought-after goal. For the first time, self-consciously experimental ships like *Triton* and *Ethalion* were built with the express purpose of improving performance under sail.

However, pure sea speed could not be pursued at the expense of other qualities, and in particular weatherliness. This may be seen in the British designers' reluctance to give up hull depth, even when adopting a French length:breadth ratio. To a lesser extent, there was also a desire to retain the British advantage in manoeuvrability, a shorter ship generally being more handy in stays, although in this they were often

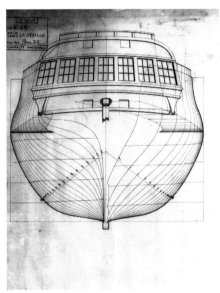

Sybille, 38 guns, ex-French, as captured sheer & profile, dated Portsmouth, 6 July 1795.

Displaying a midship section typical of the many French frigates designed by Sané, this ship was relatively shallow, even by French standards. A feature of Sané's 18pdr ships was a distinct preference for fourteen upper deck gunports a side. Thus most of his 40-gun frigates have no dedicated chase port, although the No 1 port often looks as though it was intended as such but has had a gun permanently allocated to it. In British service this ship was not an immediate success, but eventually her optimum stowage was discovered and her performance improved, although she was never as good to windward as British-built frigates.

less successful. Both may be seen as a response to the other formative experience of the 1790s, the year-round close blockade, which required ships with outstanding windward performance and responsive handling, if they were to have any chance of surviving on stations which were mostly close in, and on a lee shore. A subsidiary consideration was seakeeping, and although it is more difficult to identify, most British classes of this period were regarded as 'sea-kindly' hulls.

The improvement in performance is not great in absolute terms, but what was regarded as the norm seems to have advanced by a knot or so. By 1800 many British frigate classes were capable of 13kts with a quartering wind, but perhaps more significantly, the number capable of 10kts or more close-hauled increased. French frigates were not noticeably faster, with one or two exceptions – and those were usually larger than the standard classes. Gradually more knowledgeable officers began to realise that French 'superiority' was in fact just a different choice of priorities. Earlier chapters have pointed out the stowage difficulties of French ships on long cruises, and the relative weakness of hull construction when exposed to the rigours of blockade, but increasingly the Sailing Quality Reports contain generalisations that reflect a new awareness of performance differences: captains expected French ships to be longer in tacking and wearing, and by 1812 it was obviously a truth universally acknowledged that British hulls were more weatherly than their French equivalents.[111] In the sailing quality resumés which follow, it is possible to chart a gradual improvement, with a few relative failures, in the characteristics of British frigates; it is also clear that the *Apollo* class 36s, the large 38s of the *Lively* class, and to a lesser extent the medium 38s of the *Leda* class were the right prototypes for the ensuing mass-production programmes of the Napoleonic War.

It is perhaps curious at first sight that the 'machinery', the masts and spars, of the new enlarged classes did not grow in proportion. To some extent, this was in line with a policy of standardisation, that made for refitting efficiency even when the hull designs were being constantly varied.[112] Ultimately, a ship's power to carry sail depended on its reserve of stability, itself more influenced by breadth than any other consideration; the new larger designs tended to add length rather than breadth, so the official reluctance to add to the height and spread of the standard sail plan was probably justifiable caution.

Furthermore, it should be remembered that the conditions in which a ship could carry every scrap of sail were rarely met, so, other things being equal, the larger ships could probably stand up to their canvas longer as weather deteriorated, allowing them a *de facto* increase in sail power without any addition to the spar plan. A final consideration was the gradual augmentation of the basic sail plan, both official like the issue of a flying jib and royal staysail in 1794 and a main trysail in 1797,[113] and unofficial like the proliferation of 'flying kites' that crop up in the journals of the time; separate royal masts were introduced towards the end of the period under review, and thereafter skysails could be set flying over them. In general, the larger ships were more likely to be able to make use of these occasional sails, so an increase in the sizes of plain sails was not considered necessary. Certainly, the Navy Board did not readily alter any spar dimensions for standard frigate classes in the 1790s,[114] and the absence of petitions from captains on this score tells its own story of satisfaction with the existing establishment.

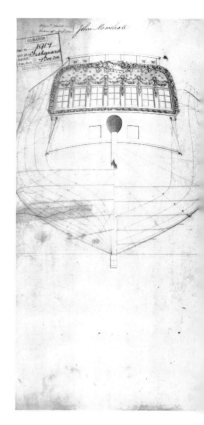

Fisgard, 38 guns, ex-French *Résistance*, as captured sheer & profile, 1797.

This wildly experimental ship incorporated many eccentric features in a very sharp hull. At the steps of the fore and main masts can be seen the screwjacks that were designed to allow a radical alteration in the rake of the masts. The V-section midship is combined with a scow-like bow and a steeply raked sternpost in a hull that trimmed heavily by the stern. Little is known about her performance in this original state, but she seems to have suffered some of the shortcomings of the later Symondite ships, being a quick and heavy roller. She was originally armed with 24pdrs, and the lighter 18pdrs fitted in British service probably compounded the rolling problem.

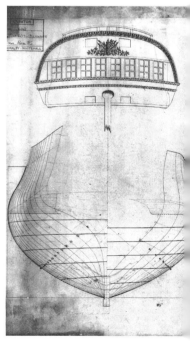

Révolutionnaire, 38 guns, ex-French, as captured sheer & profile draught (with intended British fittings in pencil), dated Portsmouth, 12 February 1795.

Another 'non-standard' French 40, with a very long, sharp-lined hull, accommodating fifteen gunports with ease (even if one was designated a chase port). The ship was fast when young, but the hull was weak and this may account for the need to cut down the rig in later life. There were also frequent complaints about the lack of stowage capacity in the fine-lined hull.

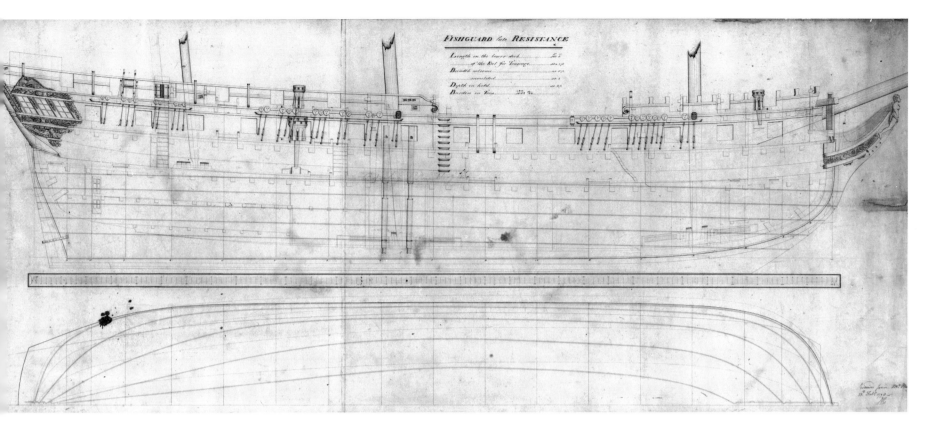

FISHGUARD late RESISTANCE

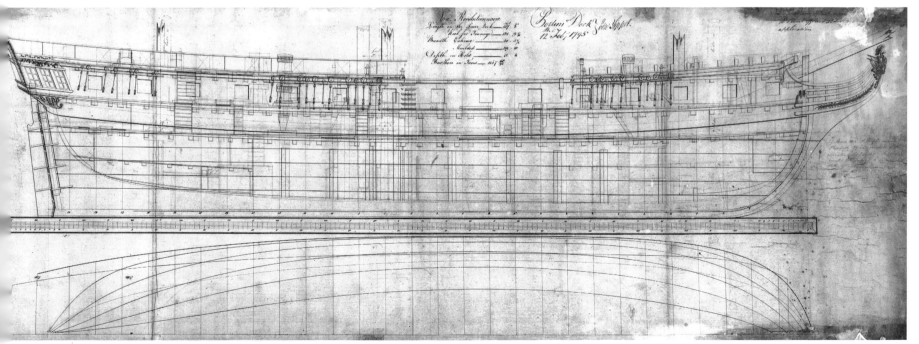

Table 56: MAST AND SPAR DIMENSIONS OF BRITISH FRIGATES

		38-gun ships			36-gun ships (as built)			36-gun ships (Flora, 1805)		32-gun ships		
		Length yds	ins	Diam ins	Length yds	ins	Diam ins	Length yds ins	Diam ins	Length yds	ins	Diam ins
MASTS												
Main	mast	30	0	27	29	23	26		29	29	0	25¼
	topmast	18	0	16⅛	17	28	15¾			17	12	15¼
	topgallant	9	0	9	8	20	8⅝			8	24	8⅝
Fore	mast	27	18	23⅝	26	24	23⅜		25⅝	26	16	22¼
	topmast	15	34	16⅛	15	23	15¾			15	12	15¼
	topgallant	7	29	7¾	7	17	7½			7	24	7½
Mizzen	mast	21	25	18½	24	32	17¾		19½	21	0	16¾
	topmast	13	24	11⅞	13	12	11⅛			13	3	10½
	topgallant	6	30	6⅞	[6	26	6¾]					
Bowsprit		18	6	26½	18	14	26⅜			18	0	26
Jibboom		13	5	11¾	12	31	11⅛			12	22	10⅞
Flying jibboom		[10	34	6½]	[10	26	6½]			[10	8	6⅛]
YARDS												
Main	yard	27	9	18⅞	26	17	18⅝			26	0	18
	topsail	19	24	12¼	19	2	12			19	8	12
	topgallant	12	18	7½	11	21	7¼			11	26	7¼
	[royal]	[9	24	6⅛]	[9	12	6]					
Fore	yard	23	29	16⅜	23	4	16			22	25	15¾
	topsail	17	28	11½	17	9	11			16	33	10⅜
	topgallant	10	35	6½	10	18	6⅜			10	12	6¼
	[royal]	[8	24	5¾]	[8	12	5½]					
Mizzen	crossjack	17	28	11½	17	9	11			16	33	10⅜
	topsail	13	20	8¼	13	4	7⅜			12	30	7¼
	topgallant	9	12	5½	[9	0	5½]					
	[royal]	[6	24	4⅛]	[6	12	3⅞]					
	(lateen)	(24	14	13⅛)	23	30	12⅞					
	gaff	12	34	11½	[12	0	11]			11	32	10⅛
	boom	[19	24	11½]	[19	0	11]					
Spritsail		17	28	11½	17	9	11			16	33	10⅜
Sprit topsail		10	35	6½	10	18	6⅜			10	12	6¼

Notes:

38-gun ships. Dimensions for *Artois* class, 6 Aug 1794 (NMM POR/A/37), but effectively the same as those for the first 38s of 1778 (NMM SPB/15), except that the mizzen (25yds 7ins, 17⅛in diam) stepped in the hold and not the lower deck and had not had its diameter increased to compensate for the newly introduced driver boom (by Admiralty Order of 29 Jun 1780). These dimensions were also specified for *Active* and *Leda* in Jan 1797 (NMM CHA/K/1) so appear to have been standard for the whole period under review.

36-gun ships. Dimensions relate to *Perseverance* (PRO Adm 106/3319, 8 May 1781), *Unicorn* and *Phoenix* (PRO Adm 95/96, 10 Jul 1781) and *Flora* c1785 (NMM SPB 37b); only *Perseverance* and *Flora* have mizzen topgallant dimensions quoted, the latter including a 6yds 3ins version with 2yds 20in pole head. The second column, with lower masts of increased diameter were as carried by *Flora* before her service as a troopship (PRO Adm 106/3103, 23 Feb 1805).

32-gun ships. Official dimensions for new 32s 'building in the neighbourhood of Southampton' – *Cerberus*, *Lively* and *Galatea* (NMM POR/A/36, 17 May 1793). The experimental *Triton* employed the same yard dimensions, although her masts were taller.

Table 57: MAST AND SPAR DIMENSIONS OF CAPTURED FRIGATES

MASTS		Révolutionnaire 28 Feb 1795			Virginie 15 Apr 1803			Minerve 6 Jul 1802			Unité, ex-Impérieuse 2 Mar 1805		
		Length yds	ins	Diam ins	Length yds	ins	Diam ins	Length yds	ins	Diam ins	Length yds	ins	Diam ins
Main	mast	30	0	27	29	19	31½			29¾	30	0	27
	topmast	18	0	16⅛	17	34	17⅛				18	0	16⅛
	topgallant	9	0	9	8	33	9⅛				9	0	9
Fore	mast	27	22	23¾	27	14	26½			26¾	26	15	23¾
	topmast	15	30	16⅛	16	16	17				15	30	16⅛
	topgallant	7	33	7⅞	8	14	8⅝				7	33	7⅞
Mizzen	mast	21	19	18¼	21	30	18¾			19⅞	25	13	18¼
	topmast	13	18	11¾	13	20	10¾				13	18	11¼
	topgallant	6	27	6¾	6	22	6⅝				6	27	6¾
Bowsprit		18	22	27¼	18	15	26½				18	22	27¼
Jibboom		13	1	11⅝	14	19	12¾				13	1	11⅝
Flying jibboom													
YARDS													
Main	yard	26	34	23¾	27	26	19½			16	26	34	18⅝
	topsail	19	24	12¼	20	0	13½			11½	19	24	12¼
	topgallant [royal]	12	18	7½	12	2	7½	10	32		12	0	7⅛
Fore	yard	23	29	16⅜	24	7	16⅝				23	19	16¼
	topsail	17	20	11	17	23	11⅝				17	20	11
	topgallant [royal]	10	24	6⅜	10	24	7¾				10	24	6⅜
Mizzen	crossjack	17	20	11	17	23	11⅝				17	20	11
	topsail	13	12	8	13	13	9⅛			8¼	13	12	8
	topgallant [royal]	9	12	5¼	9	14	5¾				9	12	5¼
	gaff boom	12	10	11½	14	11	10			11½	12	20	11½
Spritsail		17	20	11	18	19	10½			11½	17	20	11
Sprit topsail		10	24	6⅜	-	-	-	10	32		10	24	6⅜

Notes:

Révolutionnaire. Despite being far larger this ship is masted very like a standard British 38, most differences being reductions; however, the dimensions are close enough to suggest that the yard was making the best use of available timber rather than making fine adjustments to the sail plan. (NMM POR/A/38)

Virginie. Different enough from a standard 38 to suggest customising, but not the significantly larger sail plan to be expected if David Steel's formula (L+B/2 = main mast length) is applied; this works for the ships of the 1770s and 1780s but not later. (PRO Adm 106/3328)

Minerve. Variations from dimensions of a standard British 38 noted; the same were used for *Africaine*, 6 Sep 1802. (PRO Adm 106/3327)

Unité. Had been masted as a 36, and these dimensions were taken from the *Thalia, ex-Unicorn* as ordered by the Navy Board on 6 Sep 1804. Interestingly, the main mast dimensions are those of a standard 38 and the remainder are generally between the old 36 and 38 established dimensions.

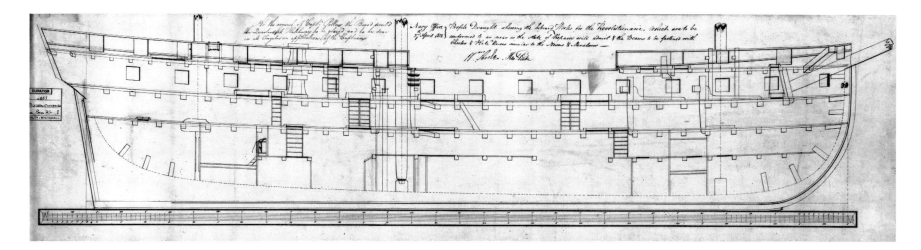

Table 58: SAILING QUALITIES OF ENGLISH FRIGATES

The following summaries of sailing qualities are preceded by examples of trim, quoting the resulting freeboard of the midships gunport (an important expression of a frigate's ability to fight in all weathers). Wherever possible, the lightest and deepest loadings are given to show the range, and the time and service for which stored (CS = Channel Service and FS = Foreign Service). The main elements of lading – iron and shingle ballast, and water– are also noted for each trim where known. There are inconsistencies and it is clear that measurement was by no means precise. After 1814 iron water tanks were gradually introduced; these not only carried more water for a given volume of hold (no space was lost as between barrels), but required no shingle to bed them down securely. This could have a significant impact on trim, and a few examples are given to demonstrate the effect.

In the descriptions of sailing qualities, the points of sailing (running, reaching, etc) are those familiar to the modern yachtsman, rather than the terminology of the time.

Minerva class, 38 guns, 1778

| | Draught (ft-ins) | | Freeboard (ft-ins) | Ballast (tons) | | | Victualled |
	Fwd	aft	midships port	Iron	shingle	water	for
Thetis	17-3	18-6	8-3	80	125	103	4 months [CS]
Phaeton							
(1783)	17-10	18-11	7-4	85	167	115	6 months [FS]
(1818)	17-10	19-2	6-7	120	–	130	4 months [CS]

Good, if not outstanding, performers under sail: 7-9kts close-hauled in topgallant gale (or up to 10kts in smooth water), 11-12kts quartering or before the wind, occasionally reaching 12½kts. However, they enjoyed the traditional British virtues of good handling and seakeeping, were stiff under sail and weatherly. Comparatively, they were not as good close-hauled as sailing large, but their real disadvantage was the tendency to pitch in heavy weather and that they were wet forward – the Phaeton's captain mentions moving the foremost pair of 18pdrs aft to ease the ship in a seaway. They probably seemed more impressive when first built, but rising expectations of performance in the 1790s led to more reserved judgements on their abilities.

Based on reports on Minerva (May 1794 and 31 Jul 1797); Arethusa (13 Apr 1802); Phaeton (16 Aug 1786, 27 Nov 1788 and 19 Mar 1818); Thetis (1 Apr 1786 and undated c1795). Later reports, when serving as troopships, have been ignored.

Révolutionnaire, 38 guns, ex-French, profile draught for repairs, dated 27 April 1812.

The rearranged internal works following a major repair; the beams are 'to be fastened with chocks and plate knees similar to the Nisus and Menelaus' (two Lively class 38s which incorporated a number of modifications, including this method of avoiding wooden knees). As with many French prizes, the main magazine is aft, with a smaller hanging magazine forward. Note the lack of headroom on the lower deck – scarcely more than 5ft between the beams.

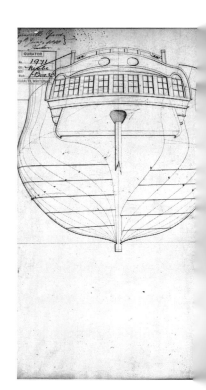

Niobe, 38 guns, ex-French Diane, as fitted sheer & profile draught, dated Plymouth, 13 June 1810.

One of Sané's 40-gun frigates that were effectively the standard of the period; they grew from 150ft to 155ft on the lower deck, but the hull form remained constant. This draught demonstrates the effect of a major British repair: all the topside detail conforms to Royal Navy practice and the layout of the internal works, with a large hanging magazine forward and a small one aft, is similar to that employed in contemporary Leda class 38s, themselves based on a Sané hull form. The ship was a good all-round performer under sail, which is probably the secret of Sané's success – there were no extreme or outstanding characteristics obtained at the expense of more practical considerations like seakeeping.

Latona, 38 guns, 1779

	Draught (ft-ins)		Freeboard (ft-ins)	Ballast (tons)			Victualled
	Fwd	aft	midships port	Iron	shingle	water	for
(1783)	17-9	17-10	7-7½	70	170	117	6 months [FS]

Generally similar from speed and handling points of view to the *Minerva*s, but not so weatherly unless the wind was strong; fast but like the *Minerva*s wet in heavy weather, although tending to ship water in the waist rather than over the bows, which in this ship rose better to a head sea. Both classes stowed their provisions well, 6 months' (except bread) being stowable under hatches.

Based on reports of 13 Jul 1784, 19 Oct 1786 and Oct 1802.

Flora class, 36 guns, 1778

	Draught (ft-ins)		Freeboard (ft-ins)	Ballast (tons)			Victualled
	Fwd	aft	midships port	Iron	shingle	water	for
Flora	18-2	18-6	7-0	73	164	69	6 months [FS]
Crescent	16-8	18-6	7-4	90	80	91	4 months [CS]

Evidence for the performance of this class as frigates is thin, since most surviving Sailing Quality Reports cover the ships while serving as troopships. However, they were certainly not fast: 8-9kts close-hauled in a topgallant gale could be achieved in smooth water and 10-11kts large (exceptionally, *Crescent* once registered 12½kts before the wind), but their speed was much affected by high seas and they also became more leewardly. However, they were excellent sea-boats and, if slow, were dry and easy in heavy weather. This made them good gun platforms, and their fighting qualities were enhanced by robust construction, exceptional gunport freeboard for their day, and handiness under sail (being quick and sure in tacking).

Based on reports on *Romulus* (22 Mar 1798) and *Crescent* (undated, 1790s); also entries in PRO Adm 180/24 and NMM RUSI/NM/74.

Perseverance class, 36 guns, 1779

	Draught (ft-ins)		Freeboard (ft-ins)	Ballast (tons)			Victualled
	Fwd	aft	midships port	Iron	shingle	water	for
Phoenix	17-10	19-6	7-1	95	75	98	6 months [FS]
Inconstant	17-6	18-4	8-0	87	130	110	4 months [CS]

As for the previous class, evidence is scanty but when the 870-ton 36 was revived in 1801 it was this design that was adopted, which should suggest that they had some advantage over the *Flora*s. However, the revival had little to do with their performance under sail and, indeed, their recorded speeds are much the same as the *Flora* class (and somewhat less late in their careers). They were similarly manoeuvrable, but much affected by heavy seas; they were regarded as leewardly and relatively crank by later standards – in 1813 *Inconstant* was specifically described as 'much inferior to the frigates of the present day'.

Based on reports on *Inconstant* (29 Apr 1808 and 1 Mar 1813) and *Phoenix* (undated *c*1790s, 12 Oct 1808 and 1 Jan 1813); also entries in PRO Adm 180/24 and NMM RUSI/NM/74.

Melampus, 36 guns, 1782

	Draught (ft-ins)		Freeboard (ft-ins)	Ballast (tons)			Victualled
	Fwd	aft	midships port	Iron	shingle	water	for
(1790)	17-10	19-4	7-1	95	140	139	4 months [CS]
(1811)	18-0	20-8	7-6				6 months [FS]

Based on the *Minerva* hull form and retaining the 38's mast and spar dimensions, this ship was roughly comparable under sail (9kts close-hauled in topgallant weather, 12kts large and 11½kts before the wind), but was easier and pitched less. She was also reckoned to be more weatherly with much improved performance to windward.

Based on report of 1 Jan 1811.

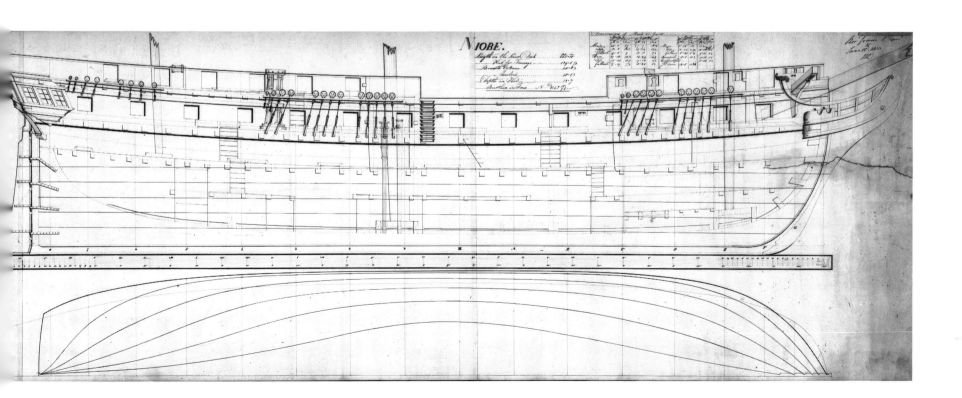

Beaulieu, 36 guns, 1790

	Draught (ft-ins) Fwd	aft	Freeboard (ft-ins) midships port	Ballast (tons) Iron	shingle	water	Victualled for
(1800)	18-10	20-2	8-3	134	238	207	4 months [CS]

There are no surviving Sailing Quality Reports for this ship.

Pallas/Alcmene classes, 32 guns, 1790/1793

	Draught (ft-ins) Fwd	aft	Freeboard (ft-ins) midships port	Ballast (tons) Iron	shingle	water	Victualled for
Stag	16-4	17-2	7-8½	80	105	70	4 months [CS]
Cerberus	16-10	18-8	7-6	113	100	90	4 months [CS]

Only an additional 6in to the beam separates these two classes and they share very similar characteristics. The slim surviving evidence suggests that *Unicorn* may have been marginally faster than her half-sisters (9kts close-hauled, 12½kts large, which is ½-1kt more than recorded for the others), but they certainly share more significant attributes. The reports all date from a period when the heavy long 18pdrs had been replaced and no complaint is made of their sea-kindliness; indeed they were particularly good sea-boats in most conditions, and were very handy (their tacking was certain even in heavy seas). They were weatherly rather than fast and this comparative advantage increased as the weather worsened; however, they were vulnerable to a head sea 'more than the generality of frigates', being retarded by their heavy pitching.

Based on reports on *Unicorn* (9 Jan 1803 and 1 Oct 1814); *Galatea* 23 Dec 1802 and 13 Mar 1809); *Cerberus* (5 Mar 1803).

Artois class, 38 guns, 1793

	Draught (ft-ins) Fwd	aft	Freeboard (ft-ins) midships port	Ballast (tons) Iron	shingle	water	Victualled for
Diana	17-2	19-3	8-1	80	180	92	4 months [CS]
Seahorse	18-9	20-8	7-1	80	160	106	6 months [FS]
Clyde [fir]	15-10	18-8	8-10½	130	109	140	4 months [CS]

Initial reaction to this class was favourable – Sir Edward Nagle, for example, thought *Artois* the best sailing ship in Sir John Borlase Warren's crack frigate squadron[115] - but from a speed point of view they were no improvement over the *Minervas*: 9kts close-hauled in a topgallant gale is the best recorded and 11-12kts large or before the wind. *Seahorse* registered 13kts on one occasion, but on the captain's admission only briefly before she was forced to shorten sail. They were somewhat overshadowed by later classes of superior performance and considered opinion found them good but not exceptional: *Diamond* was described as 'a fair sailing ship, but never remarked her to be so fast a sailer as some men of war'; *Diana* was similarly 'fair', while *Seahorse* compared with other ships 'pretty even but not a prime sailer'. Some doubts were expressed about their windward qualities as built but an additional false keel made them more weatherly. However, they were very handy, being quick and sure in stays, and were reasonably stiff under their canvas. As sea-boats their one major drawback was a tendency to pitch excessively when carrying sail through a head sea, so this fault of the *Minervas* had not been ameliorated.

There are no surviving Sailing Quality Reports on the fir ships, but a letter from the captain of the *Clyde* suggests she was handy and fast, particularly large, although somewhat leewardly close-hauled; speeds quoted in one list suggest they were a knot faster than their oak sisters on all points of sailing. Both ships were highly regarded by their captains.

Based on reports on *Artois* (24 Jul 1794); *Diana* (Jan and 1 May 1812); *Diamond* (29 Sep 1809); *Seahorse* (undated c1790s and 12 Sep 1815); and NMM ADM/A/ 2883, letter of 17 Aug 1796; NMM RUSI/NM/74.

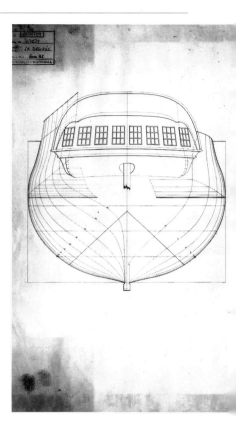

Desirée, 36 guns, ex-French, as fitted sheer & profile draught, dated Sheerness 1800.

An odd vessel that seems not to have been built for the navy; she was certainly smaller that the contemporary frigates and the hull form is unlike the work of other French naval constructors. She was not very weatherly and a note on the draught concerns a sketch sent 'to Sheerness 20 January '12 for bringing on an additional gripe and false keel', easily seen on the draught because it drops below the top of the scale.

Phoebe class, 36 guns, 1794

	Draught (ft-ins) Fwd	aft	Freeboard (ft-ins) midships port	Ballast (tons) Iron	shingle	water	Victualled for
Phoebe	19-6	20-4	6-9	106	50	110	6 months [FS]
Dryad (1795)	17-2	18-8	7-8½	85	185	91	4 months [CS]
Dryad (1829)	17-7	19-0	8-2	115	0	120	6 months [FS]

In this class the *Inconstant* hull form was lengthened to improve performance and this was certainly achieved from the viewpoint of pure speed: they were capable of 10kts close-hauled and 12-13kts large. They were generally weatherly and retained the handiness of the earlier ships but sacrificed their seakeeping for speed. They were somewhat crank and could not be pressed, particularly in heavier weather, when they were subject to heavy pitching. The first report on *Fortunee*, which had a modified bow, did not complain of pitching but later she is characterised as 'an uneasy ship but weatherly'. The trim data above for the *Dryad* demonstrate the effect of iron water tanks, which banished the need for shingle. This allowed ships to trim less deep (with increased gunport freeboard) but since the water was stowed low in the hull it offered the prospect of improved stability – or at least, rather more control over the effects of stowage on stability. Interestingly, by 1829 the problem of crankness in *Dryad* was under control, the ship being 'soon down to her bearings but then stands well'.

Based on reports on *Dryad* (Jun 1829); *Phoebe* (25 Jan 1812, 31 Dec 1812 and 28 Aug 1815); *Fortunee* (8 Oct 1802, 10 Jan 1812, 20 Feb 1813 and 11 Jan 1814).

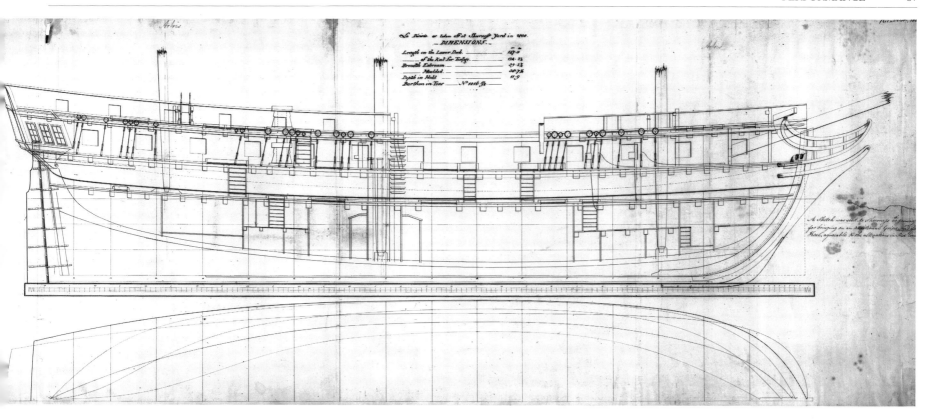

Amazon class, 36 guns, 1794

	Draught (ft-ins)		Freeboard (ft-ins)	Ballast (tons)			Victualled
	Fwd	aft	midships port	Iron	shingle	water	for
Amazon	17-3	19-0	7-10½	90	160	95	4 months [CS]
Glenmore [fir]	17-0	19-0	7-11	140	185	97	4 months [CS]

Judging by the *Emerald*, the oak ships were disappointing under sail, not registering more than 9kts close-hauled and 11kts large, even if they were weatherly and manoeuvrable. As a sea-boat their worst characteristic was a tendency to heavy pitching in a head sea and in general they seem to have been sensitive to bad weather. The fir ships were significantly faster off the wind, *Glenmore* making 13kts before the wind, but although much stiffer were not quite so fast as the hardwood ships close-hauled; they also handled well in smooth water but did not like heavy weather and were prone to the same pitching.

Based on reports on *Emerald* (7 Apr 1805); *Trent* (14 Jun 1809); *Glenmore* (25 Jan 1803).

Sirius, 36 guns, 1795

	Draught (ft-ins)		Freeboard (ft-ins)	Ballast (tons)			Victualled
	Fwd	aft	midships port	Iron	shingle	water	for
(1798)	18-2	19-3	7-2	90	160	95	4 months [CS]
(1802)	17-10	19-0	7-6	85	110	94	4 months [CS]

Had the mast and spars of the 38-gun class. A fast ship in heavier weather that regularly ran 13kts with all sail set going large and could manage 10kts close-hauled in a stiff breeze; she was also weatherly and could also maintain speed better than most in stronger conditions – 5-6kts on a bowline into a head sea in a gale was a good achievement. She was also easy and very dry in a seaway, and although generally handy was considered slack in stays (on the other hand, she had often been tacked under courses alone, which few ships could manage). Surprisingly, for a hull of French proportions, she stowed her provisions well.

Based on report of 3 Aug 1802.

Naiad, 38 guns, 1795

	Draught (ft-ins)		Freeboard	Ballast (tons)			Victualled
	Fwd	aft	midships port	Iron	shingle	water	for
(1798)	17-4	19-1	8-2	96	110	105	3 months [CS]
	19-0	20-9	7-0	105	85	125	4 months [CS]
	19-10	21-8	6-7				6 months [FS]

A fast ship in heavy weather on all points of sailing, achieving 13kts off the wind and 10kts close-hauled but needing a press of sail; also much retarded by a head sea, which caused heavy pitching. Poor in light conditions. Not very handy, steering, tacking and wearing 'but tolerably well'. Capacious, being able to stow 6 months' provisions in the after hold. The captain's considered opinion was 'a good and serviceable, but somewhat unwieldy ship, ill suited to a shoally coast from her heavy draught. Not sailing very well compared with other frigates, but compensating by being easy, weatherly, roomy and unusually stiff under canvas.' Masts and spars were increased by Admiralty Order of 6 November 1799.

Based on report of 1 Feb 1812.

Boadicea, 38 guns, 1795

	Draught (ft-ins)		Freeboard	Ballast (tons)			Victualled
	Fwd	aft	midships port	Iron	shingle	water	for
	17-3	18-7	7-1	72	40	111	months [CS]
	17-9	19-3	6-8	94	0	112	6 months [FS]

Average under sail, not recording more than 9kts close-hauled and 11½kts off the wind. A good sea-boat but although easy she pitched deep; only 'tolerably' handy in staying and wearing. In 1799 additions to her gripe and an extra 4in were added to her false keel, suggesting that as built her windward performance was unsatisfactory.

Based on report of Aug 1827; NMM RUSI/NM/74; PRO Adm 180/24.

Hydra, 38 guns, 1795

	Draught (ft-ins)		Freeboard	Ballast (tons)			Victualled
	Fwd	aft	midships port	Iron	shingle	water	for
(1798)	17-6	18-5	7-3	110	112	85	4 months [CS]
(1815)	17-3	18-4	8-3	136	0	112	4 months [CS]

Surviving reports date from the ship's period on trooping duties, so cannot be taken as representative of performance as a frigate; the main features are summarised for interest. Only a moderate performer, recording 9kts close-hauled in topgallant weather and 12kts large; stiff under her canvas but only averagely weatherly. She was generally responsive, although slow in wearing and was a very good easy sea-boat; stowed 6 months' provisions well without having to take out any ballast.

Based on undated report (c1814) and one of 6 Nov 1815 when the ship was serving as a troopship and rigged as a 24-gun ship.

Triton, 32 guns, 1796

	Draught (ft-ins)		Freeboard	Ballast (tons)			Victualled
	Fwd	aft	midships port	Iron	shingle	water	for
	16-6	16-6	7-10	200	100	?	4 months [CS]
	16-3	16-3	7-8	165	94	70	4 months [CS]

A fast ship that had gone 10½kts close-hauled under double-reefed topsails, she had a decided superiority in heavier conditions, but was sometimes beaten in moderate winds and smooth water. She was not, however, very weatherly and the captain advocated an addition to her false keel. She was a heavy roller due to so much ballast but easy on her rigging and stiff enough to carry canvas when most ships shortened sail. The shape of the bow kept her very dry but tended to 'slam' into a sea, throwing the stern down and making her vulnerable to a following sea in bad weather. Once the fore mast had been moved forward, she was responsive and handy.

Based on Captain's report 21 Jul 1797, from Lor[...]Admiralty Secretary, forwarded to Navy Board, NMM ADM/A/289[...]

Active, 38 guns, 1796

	Draught (ft-ins)		Freeboard (ft-ins)	Ballast (tons)			Victualled
	Fwd	aft	midships port	Iron	shingle	water	for
(as built)	17-10	18-10	7-10	116	70	90	4 months [CS]
(with tanks)	17-11	18-6	8-0	130	0	124	6 months [FS]

This 'modified Artois' was perhaps a trifle faster, although regarded as rather leewardly. Easier sea-boat than the earlier design, but lacking initial stiffness, although once heeled a couple of strakes she then stood up well to her canvas. Could stow 107 tons of water (124 tons after tanks fitted) with 6 months' provisions under hatches (except for 1 month's bread).

Based on reports of 9 Oct 1817 and one undated (possibly later).

Amazon class, 38 guns, 1796

	Draught (ft-ins)		Freeboard (ft-ins)	Ballast (tons)			Victualled
	Fwd	aft	midships port	Iron	shingle	water	for
Hussar	18-1	19-8	7-6	120	98	110	4 months [CS]
Amazon	19-5	20-2	6-8	150	132	118	4 months [CS]
Amazon	19-6	20-3	6-6½				6 months [FS]

Fast and very weatherly, achieving 10kts close-hauled in a topgallant gale and 13kts large; superiority compared with other ships was most marked on a wind in a stiff breeze. Manoeuvrable, if rather long in wearing, but principal fault was deep and uneasy rolling and pitching; very stiff, which may have been the root of the problem. Stowed 6 months' provisions (except bread) with ease.

Based on reports on Amazon (31 Dec 1811 and 15 Feb 1812).

Leda class, 38 guns, 1796

	Draught (ft-ins)		Freeboard (ft-ins)	Ballast (tons)			Victualled
	Fwd	aft	midships port	Iron	shingle	water	for
Leda	17-0	18-8	7-1	90	80	92	4 months [CS]

Considering so many ships were built to this design, it is difficult to discern any outstanding advantages – at least, judging from the early ships. It is clear that they were very fast, particularly in strong winds when they could easily manage 13kts with a beam or following wind and 10kts close-hauled; but they were not very weatherly and Shannon for one was improved by an addition to the false keel. Captain Broke, who had been in command for six years, thought Shannon was a sensitive ship requiring careful handling, but responsive when so treated. There was also a questionmark over their seakeeping since they were heavy, if easy, rollers. They had shallower hulls than the British norm and were complained of for not stowing more than 4 months' provisions under hatches and then could not carry 3 months' water. The ships built by Brindley and Pelham were of light fastening, constructed without knees, and needed considerable attention in later life – the topsides of Broke's ship were said to 'work like a basket'.

Based on NMM RUSI/NM/74 and reports on Shannon (17 Jun 1812) ; Leonidas (5 Feb 1812, 1 Jan 1814, 1 Jan 1815 and 19 Jun 1815).

Amphion class, 32 guns, 1796

	Draught (ft-ins)		Freeboard (ft-ins)	Ballast (tons)			Victualled
	Fwd	aft	midships port	Iron	shingle	water	for
Amphion	16-6	17-10	7-6	90	60	100	4 months [CS]
	17-6	18-8	7-0	90	50	90	6 months [FS]
(with tanks)	17-3	18-6	7-2	170	0	118	4 months [CS]
	17-6	18-8	7-0	170	0	110	6 months [FS]

Excellent all-round ships: fast and very weatherly, regularly attaining 10kts close-hauled and 13kts large in a stiff breeze and relatively smooth water. Very stiff, they could carry sail well but tended to show more advantage over other ships when there was no big sea running; fairly lively but easy sea-boats, with a tendency to pitching in a head sea that made them sensitive to weight in the bows. Quick in stays and wearing and responsive to the helm. Stowed 6 months' provisions without trouble.

Based on reports on Amphion (24 Jan 1803, 22 Aug 1815, 31 Dec 1817, 1 Jan and 20 May 1819); Medusa (Feb 1806); Aeolus (24 [month illegible] 1812, undated c1814); Nereus (11 Jan 1815).

Penelope class, 36 guns, 1797

	Draught (ft-ins)		Freeboard (ft-ins)	Ballast (tons)			Victualled
	Fwd	aft	midships port	Iron	shingle	water	for
Penelope	16-10	17-11	8-3½	85	160	115	5 months [FS]
Amethyst	17-2	18-6	7-5½	110	100	91	4 months [CS]

There are no surviving reports on these ships, but the little evidence suggests that they were not outstanding: Penelope is credited in two lists with 8-9kts close-hauled, 11kts large and 12kts before the wind. Other characteristics will be available if the compiler's symbols in these lists are ever deciphered.

Based on NMM RUSI/NM/74 and PRO Adm 180/24.

Narcissus class, 32 guns, 1798

	Draught (ft-ins)		Freeboard (ft-ins)	Ballast (tons)			Victualled
	Fwd	aft	midships port	Iron	shingle	water	for
Narcissus	17-6	18-7	7-6	120	60	90	4 months [CS]
Tartar	16-8	17-1	8-2	90	110	86	4 months [CS]

Weatherly and reasonably fast (9kts close-hauled, 12kts large, 11kts before the wind) but 'the best sailing ships beat Narcissus', although she had the advantage of

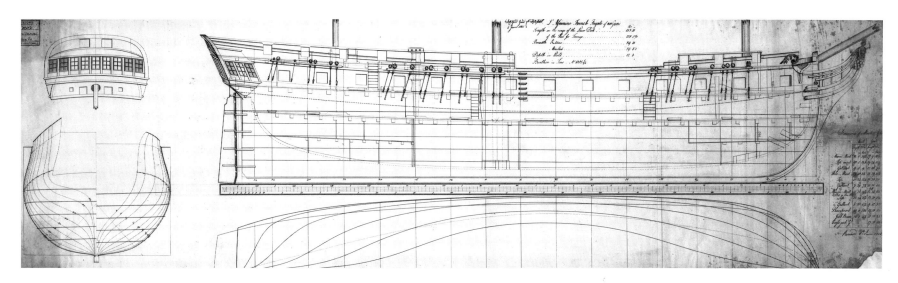

the average run of vessels. They were clearly not as fast as the *Amphion*s but were very good, easy sea-boats, and particularly quick in staying and wearing. They stowed 4 months' victuals under hatches but there is no information on how they coped with 6 months' Foreign Service allocation.

Based on reports on *Narcissus* (14 Jan & 12 Mar 1812).

Apollo class, 36 guns, 1798

	Draught (ft-ins)		Freeboard (ft-ins)	Ballast (tons)			Victualled
	Fwd	aft	midships port	Iron	shingle	water	for
Apollo	17-8	19-2	7-2	110	140	135	4 months [CS]
Apollo	17-10	19-4	7-0	110	140	125	6 months [FS]

Better than average ships with a notably good performance to windward, being both fast and weatherly, particularly in heavier conditions. *Apollo* was 'supposed to be among the fastest ships in the Service', while *Euryalus* had logged 12kts sailing large in a topgallant gale under single reefed topsails and 9½kts under treble reefed topsails and foresail alone. They were generally good for 9-10kts close-hauled in a topgallant breeze. Not overly stiff, so easy in their motions; fast and dependable in manoeuvring, if a little long in wearing. Very capacious, able to stow 6 months' provisions under hatches.

Based on reports on *Apollo* (9 Apr 1802) and *Euryalus* (28 Aug 1815) checked against reports on the later ships *Semiramis* (1 Jan 1812, Aug 1814 & 23 Sep 1818); *Malacca* (13 Jul 1815); *Owen Glendower* (11 May 1816).

Aigle class, 36 guns, 1798

	Draught (ft-ins)		Freeboard (ft-ins)	Ballast (tons)			Victualled
	Fwd	aft	midships port	Iron	shingle	water	for
Aigle	17-0	19-4	8-0	84	80	105	4 months [CS]

Generally similar to *Apollo*, being fast and weatherly, manoeuvrable and a good sea-boat. Recorded 10kts close-hauled in a topgallant gale and had gone faster (10½kts) in a stronger whole topsail wind; 12kts with the wind a point abaft the beam was best regular performance. Very roomy but no information on how they stowed 6 months' victuals.

Based on report on *Aigle* (15 Aug 1815).

Africaine, 38 guns, ex-French, as captured (?) sheer & profile draught, dated Deptford, 6 June 1802.

A very different hull form from the Sané standard, this ship was designed by R A Haran, who favoured a much fuller midship section. This made the ship much more suitable for British requirements, since it stowed its provisions well and was a good heavy weather performer. The ship is a good example of a French '40' whose gunport disposition suggests thirteen real ports and a chase port, although all fourteen seem to have been permanently established with guns in both French and British service. It is notable that a ship completed in 1798 and captured in 1801 still has no provision for carronades, to judge from the small ports on quarterdeck and forecastle. A proper iron 24pdr carronade [was not] introduced to the French service until 1804, but there was a 36pd [obus]ier (a howitzer-like barrel on a slide carriage) available from [1795?]. four were formally established on the quarterdecks of 40-gun sh[ips but] were not always shipped.

Ethalion, 36 guns, 1799

	Draught (ft-ins)		Freeboard (ft-ins)	Ballast (tons)			Victualled
	Fwd	aft	midships port	Iron	shingle	water	for
Ethalion	18-10	16-6	8-0	116	70	117	4 months [CS]

This experimental ship was undoubtedly fast (11kts close-hauled, 12½kts large), manoeuvrable, spacious and dry, but could not be pressed in heavier conditions. In 1815 the captain summed up her qualities thus: 'The ship is narrow for her length, very wall sided, capacious and airy on both the upper and lower decks, but from these circumstances she lays over when under a press of sail, her draught of water makes her weatherly; when she lays over, which she does easily to a certain bearing, it is difficult to elevate the lee guns or depress the weather guns sufficiently to fight them; under low sail, she is a good ship, easy and weatherly.' This is remarkably similar to her first captain's report of 1804, so nothing had been done to make her less tender or a better gun platform.

Based on reports of 1 Jan & 12 Sep 1815, and captain's letter of 14 Oct 1804 in PRO Adm 1/2512.

continued on page 92

'*Amethyst* in chase of *Thétis*' (10 Nov 1808), watercolour by Nicholas Pocock.

As an ex-seaman Pocock had a reputation for the accuracy of his ship portraits, and since there are no known draughts of the *Amethyst* class the picture has value beyond its obvious artistic merits. Nevertheless, the bow is obscured by smoke from the chase gun, and in most respects the painting can only confirm that the class followed the usual British practice in terms of appearance. It may be better considered as a fine illustration of the typical rig of the period, although accounts of the action make it clear that about the time depicted the *Amethyst* was carrying royals and studding sails 'aloft and alow'.

The chase also throws some light on the performance of the *Amethyst*, since the *Thétis* was a good if not outstanding performer close-hauled and was sailing at 9kts after taking in studding sails; she was, nevertheless, overhauled in less than two hours by the British frigate without royals or her studding sails.

In a later engagement, in April 1809, the *Amethyst* was outrun by the

Niemèn in a close-hauled stern chase, but easily outpaced her consort the *Emerald*. The last was known to be an indifferent sailer, but *Niemèn* was good on a wind. She was supposedly even better with the wind free, but the tactical situation did not allow her to exploit the advantage. Later, when the British captain's prediction of the *Niemèn*'s intentions again brought them together, the French ship attempted to escape by sailing large and was then overtaken by *Amethyst*. In both engagements, the British ship was better handled than its opponent, but whether this indicates superior manoeuvrability is difficult to determine.

It is unwise to read too much into the scanty evidence of specific events, where there are so many unknown variables (both French frigates were heavily laden for resupply missions, for example). However, the *Amethyst* was clearly an improvement over the *Emerald*'s class, and although not top-flight was better than average; she also seems to have been better sailing large than close-hauled.

Galatea, 32 guns, stowage plan, from Sailing Quality report dated 23 Dec 1802.

From at least the middle of the eighteenth century the Royal Navy sought to improve and systematise information on the performance of its ships. The Sailing Quality reports were earlier in origin, but became more detailed as time went on, indicating that their value was increasing or at least was more widely appreciated. Much of the additional data related to stowage, trim and the setting up of masts and rigging, which, like the tuning of an engine, could make substantial differences to the performance of any ship. From the 1750s details of stowage and trim were recorded by the Dockyards whenever a ship went to sea, and during the American War recommended ballasting plans were drawn up. Nevertheless, many captains experimented with stowage and occasionally passed on the information in graphical as well as written form. This sketch was drawn on the reverse of one of *Galatea*'s Sailing Quality forms and represents the captain's view of how to obtain the optimum trim: 17ft 7ins forward, 18ft 4ins aft.

The lefthand drawing represents the hull below the orlop deck (bow to the top), with the height of the ground tier ticked inside. The starboard side shows the configuration of the iron ballast; the port side, the ground tier of water butts (holding ½ a ton each) and hogsheads (¼ ton), plus shingle ballast. The smaller sketch is the orlop platform, with the second tier of water (butts and ⅓-ton puncheons) to port, and the third (of puncheons only) to starboard; a similar fourth tier was added above the third. Total water stowed amounted to 92½ tons.

This diagram shows clearly how the weight and volume of stowage was dominated by ballast and water, and hence its crucial importance for trim, stability and power to carry sail. Not surprisingly, these figures are often quoted in the more detailed official lists of the 1790s and later. (*PRO Adm 95/41*)

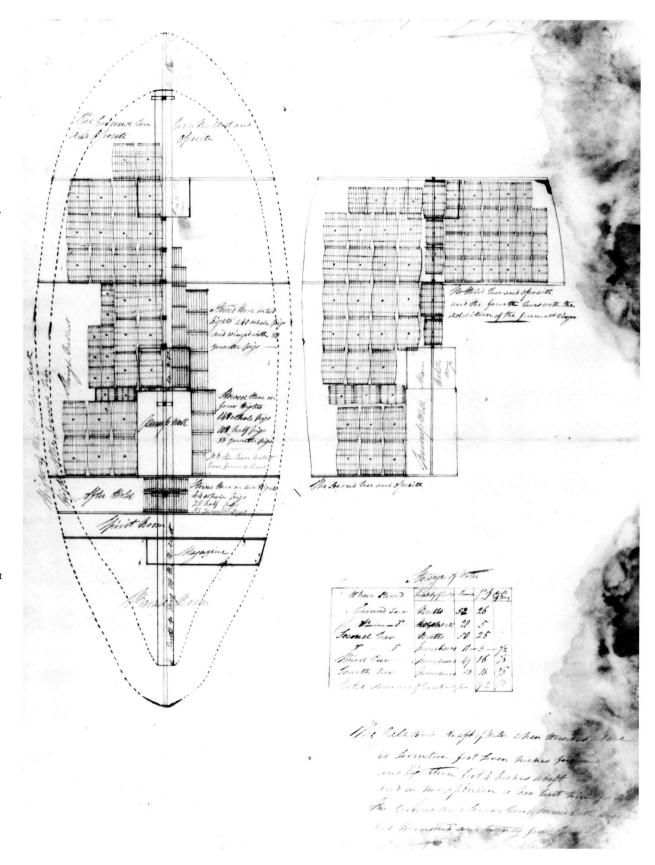

Lively class, 38 guns, 1799

| | Draught (ft-ins) | | Freeboard (ft-ins) | Ballast (tons) | | | Victualled |
	Fwd	aft	midships port	Iron	shingle	water	for
Lively	17-6	19-6	7-9	140	75	100	4 months [CS]
Undaunted	18-3	19-3	7-8½	130	50	135	6 months [FS]

Very fast and weatherly ships (11kts close-hauled and 13kts large are quoted), but they had a distinct preference for heavier conditions, being capable of 9½kts even against a head sea, but were not good in light winds. Relatively speaking, their performance to windward was their best point of sailing and they sailed best deep. Because they were stiff they were not the easiest of sea-boats, and were not especially handy because of their length, although they were dependable in stays. There were numerous complaints of the weakness of their topsides, so they seem to have been relatively lightly built, following the trend established in the *Leda* class.

There is no surviving report on *Lively* (or indeed any of the earliest ships of the class) so the above is based on reports on *Horatio* (undated c1815); *Undaunted* (1 Jan 1814 & 14 Nov 1815); *Hussar* (31 Aug 1813).

Table 59: SAILING QUALITIES OF FRENCH FRIGATES

See Table 58 for note on trim data. The French ships are organised by date of construction to allow the reader to judge whether any change in performance over time can be perceived.

Aigle, 38 guns, St Malo 1779, ?designer (captured 1782)

| | Draught (ft-ins) | | Freeboard (ft-ins) | Ballast (tons) | | | Victualled |
	Fwd	aft	midships port	Iron	shingle	water	for
(1793)	16-2	17-7	6-8	79	80		[FS] ?6 months

There are no available sailing quality reports on this ship.

Artois, 40 guns, Lorient 1780, ?designer (captured 1780)

| | Draught (ft-ins) | | Freeboard (ft-ins) | Ballast (tons) | | | Victualled |
	Fwd	aft	midships port	Iron	shingle	water	for
(1782)	16-0	17-8	7-6	105	135	87	3 months [CS]
(1781)	16-2	17-4	10-6				3 months [CS]
(1781)	16-6	17-9	10-1				6 months [FS]

Relatively fast (10kts close-hauled, 12kts large) and weatherly ship, whose best point of sailing was with the wind abeam, although she also went well on a wind. Easy sea-boat which 'behaves much better in a head sea than from her fine construction forward would be thought'. Steered and worked 'remarkably well'.

Originally masted as captured, on 27 Jun 1781 the dimensions were ordered reduced to those of a British 50-gun ship after complaint by her new captain.

Based on report of 20 Jan 1781.

Hebe, 38 guns, St Malo 1782, J N Sané (captured 1782)

| | Draught (ft-ins) | | Freeboard (ft-ins) | Ballast (tons) | | | Victualled |
	Fwd	aft	midships port	Iron	shingle	water	for
(1783)	17-4	17-3	6-10	130	50	120	3 months [CS]
(1796)	17-4	18-1	6-4				4 months [CS]
(1796)	17-9	18-10	5-11				6 months [FS]

Good all-round performer, stiff, weatherly and fast (particularly close-hauled when she logged 10½kts in a topgallant gale, but she could reach 12½kts with the wind on the quarter or aft). Her rolling was deep but easy, and she was said to steer easy and work well. The only serious drawback, as with many French frigates, was the difficulty of stowing 6 months' provisions.

Based on report of 7 Nov 1796.

San Fiorenzo, 36 guns, ex-*Minerve*, Toulon 1782, J M B Coulomb (captured 1794)

| | Draught (ft-ins) | | Freeboard (ft-ins) | Ballast (tons) | | | Victualled |
	Fwd	aft	midships port	Iron	shingle	water	for
(1795)	17-3	18-2	7-1	75	210	73	4 months [CS]
(1798)	18-3	17-9	6-8½	150	174	62	4 months [CS]

The one surviving British report is too soon after her capture to be very helpful, but suggests that the ship was not outstanding. As captured she rolled very deep but had since been restowed with iron ballast and was much easier.

The French view is that the first-generation 18pdr frigates designed by Coulomb were not quite as good as Sané's, but steered well, were stiff, and easy in their motions, but pitched heavily and were slowed by a head sea. They were ordinary sailers close-hauled, but were superior with the wind large, and tacked and wore well. Coulomb's 18pdr ships were built to a common specification, and French sources treat *Minerve*, *Junon*, *Perle*, *Impérieuse* and *Melpomène* as sister-ships, even though the British 'as captured' draughts suggest slight differences.

Based on report of 6 Dec 1794; French view from Jean Boudriot, *La Frégate*, p136.

Princess Charlotte, 36 guns, ex-*Junon*, Toulon 1782, J M B Coulomb (captured 1799)

	Draught (ft-ins)		Freeboard (ft-ins)	Ballast (tons)			Victualled
	Fwd	aft	midships port	Iron	shingle	water	for
(1814)	17-8	19-2	6-4	120	60	105	4 months [CS]
(1821)	17-10	18-10	6-8	103	-	96	4 months [CS]

Very weatherly although not exceptionally fast: 8-9kts close-hauled, 12kts large, with best point of sailing reckoned to be with a beam wind. Good sea-boat in moderate conditions, although a deep roller - under close reefed topsails and courses when blowing fresh, within 7 points of the wind would go 10kts 'and beat off any competition'. Average manoeuvrability, wearing 'as well as most ships' and tacking 'with attention' better than most.

Based on reports of 20 Jul 1814, 17 Sep 1821, and 3 Sep 1825.

Amelia, 38 guns, ex-*Proserpine*, Brest 1785, J N Sané (captured 1796)

	Draught (ft-ins)		Freeboard (ft-ins)	Ballast (tons)			Victualled
	Fwd	aft	midships port	Iron	shingle	water	for
(1803)	17-3	18-1	7-3	90	85	85	3 months [CS]
(1805)	17-3	18-6	6-9	107	26	84	6 months [FS]

For a sister-ship of the *Hebe*, the performance of this ship was surprisingly poor: 9kts close-hauled is the best recorded (and then only if the sea was smooth), and 11kts large. Her biggest shortcoming was a very bad reaction to stronger conditions: 'with a stiff gale and head sea is very leewardly'; and in similar conditions close-hauled 'sails heavy'. She was tolerably stiff and a good, easy sea-boat; quick in stays but long in wearing. Stowed more than 4 months' provisions badly.

Based on reports of 13 Jan 1803, 16 Jun 1805, and 25 Jun 1816.

Modeste, 36 guns, Toulon 1787 [12pdr ship], J M B Coulomb (captured 1793)

	Draught (ft-ins)		Freeboard (ft-ins)	Ballast (tons)			Victualled
	Fwd	aft	midships port	Iron	shingle	water	for
(1794)	14-8	16-1	7-6				3 months [CS]

Designed for 12pdrs, this ship may have been unduly burdened by the upgrading to 18pdrs. She was certainly a poor performer, being slow (6kts close-hauled, 9kts large and 10kts before the wind),and generally leewardly. Byam Martin, for whom she was his first post command, should have been charmed, but his report is damning: 'steers indifferently, wears slow, and does not stay well if there is much sea... She in general sailed worse and was less weatherly than any man of war in company'. She initially served as a convoy escort, but was rapidly reduced to a troopship, and in 1804 was made a floating battery.

Based on reports of 9 Dec 1794 (there is a later report as a troopship, which found the ship marginally faster, stiff and weatherly under her cut-down rig).

Impérieuse, 38 guns, Toulon 1787, J M B Coulomb (captured 1793)

	Draught (ft-ins)		Freeboard (ft-ins)	Ballast (tons)			Victualled
	Fwd	aft	midships port	Iron	shingle	water	for
(1796)	17-2	17-7	7-3	75	170	85	4 months [CS]

Very fast ship in lighter conditions, capable of 9½-10½kts close-hauled in a topgallant gale, and could run before the wind at 13kts under topsails alone; weatherly in these circumstances but needed to be trimmed deep. A heavy but easy roller, and a wet ship, forward and in the waist, in any seaway. Not particularly manoeuvrable, being slack in stays and long in wearing. Stowed her provisions

'fairly', and rather better than most French frigates. Robert Wilson's journal for 1805-7 confirms her speed (she beat *Hydra* in trials and later outpaced *Active* while in chase of the enemy), but also mentions her wetness in heavy weather.

Based on reports of 18 Dec 1794 and 15 Oct 1814; Wilson's journal is published in the Navy Records Society volume *Five Naval Journals, 1789-1817*, edited by Rear-Admiral H G Thursfield (London 1951).

Melpomène, 38 guns, Toulon 1789, J M B Coulomb (captured 1794)

	Draught (ft-ins)		Freeboard (ft-ins)	Ballast (tons)			Victualled
	Fwd	aft	midships port	Iron	shingle	water	for
(1795)	16-6	16-9	7-8	125	190	100	4 months [CS]

A fast and weatherly ship, particularly in moderate conditions, recording 10kts close-hauled and 13kts before the wind. Very responsive in tacking 'with helm never more than three spokes down' and wore well, although she required a lot of sea room. Described as 'peculiarly stiff', she rolled heavily before the wind, but was otherwise a good sea-boat. Stowed her provisions better than most French frigates.

Based on reports of c1798 (there is an earlier report but it pre-dates any sea experience with the ship) and Oct 1809; there are later reports (21 Jan 1812, 1 Jan 1813 and 1 Jan 1814) when the vessel was a troopship, armed *en flûte* and with reduced spars.

Sybille, 44 guns, Toulon 1791, J N Sané (captured 1794)

	Draught (ft-ins)		Freeboard (ft-ins)	Ballast (tons)			Victualled
	Fwd	aft	midships port	Iron	shingle	water	for
	18-6	19-0	5-10	109	60	112	6 months [FS]

Early reports were unenthusiastic, finding the ship weatherly but not fast (8-9kts close-hauled and about 11½kts large being the highest speeds quoted). She was also long in staying and wearing and a deep, if easy, roller. Stowed even 6 months' provisions well, although required all the ballast to be retained. She was later refitted and given lightweight 18pdrs, after which she touched much higher speeds: 10½kts close-hauled and 13kts large (although she was said to be frequently beaten on a wind by British-built frigates). In 1815 it was reported that she did not sail so well after iron water tanks had been fitted (although she gained 25 tons stowage).

Based on reports of 17 Dec 1794, undated 1790s, 8 Feb 1812, 1 Jan 1813, 19 Apr 1815, 14 Aug 1820, 1 Jan 1823 and 9 Nov 1826.

Fisgard, 38 guns, ex-*Résistance*, Paimboeuf 1793 [24pdr ship], P Degay (captured 1797)

	Draught (ft-ins)		Freeboard (ft-ins)	Ballast (tons)			Victualled
	Fwd	aft	midships port	Iron	shingle	water	for
(1799)	16-5	17-10	8-6	90	40	79	4 months [CS]
(1812)	17-8	19-2	7-7½	85	0	94	4 months [CS]

The only surviving report post-dates a major rebuilding – and quotes no speeds – so there is little that can be said about this unusual ship in her original form. The screw-jacks for altering the rake of the main and fore masts were soon removed in any case, so there was probably no British trial of their efficacy. As rebuilt the ship was very stiff, and carried her battery very high, but was a quick and heavy roller.

Based on report of 10 Nov 1809.

Révolutionnaire, 38 guns, Le Havre 1794, P A Forfait (captured 1794)

	Draught (ft-ins)		Freeboard (ft-ins)	Ballast (tons)			Victualled
	Fwd	aft	midships port	Iron	shingle	water	for
(1799)	16-9	17-4	6-8	90	40	98	4 months [CS]
(1816)	17-3	19-4	6-7	107	0	86	4 months [FS]
(1822)	15-11	18-3	7-3	65	0	86	3 months [CS]

The 1822 report makes it clear that the ship had been considered a flyer – she once ran 129 miles in 9½ hours averaging 13½kts[116] – but despite having tried every variation of stowage and rake of mast, her current officers found her 'not equal to our expectations' sailing against other ships. They believed it was because her spars had been cut down 7-8ft to those of a 42-gun frigate (the old 36) from a 50. However, even the 1808 report gives no higher speed than 12½kts large and 9½kts close-hauled. In general, she was regarded as stiff and weatherly, a good sea-boat and, for such a long ship, relatively handy. Her biggest drawback was the lack of stowage, 4 months' provisions and 86 tons of water being the maximum possible (a British-built ship of the same size would expect to stow 130-140 tons of water).

Based on reports of 18 Feb 1808, Dec 1816 and 4 Jul 1822.

Virginie, 38 guns, Brest 1794, J N Sané (captured 1796)

	Draught (ft-ins)		Freeboard (ft-ins)	Ballast (tons)			Victualled
	Fwd	aft	midships port	Iron	shingle	water	for
(1790s)	17-6	19-0	5-8	130	60	93	4 months [CS]
(c1814)	17-5	18-7	6-8	114	0	82	3 months [CS]

Fast off the wind (12-13kts), and moderate close-hauled (9kts); weatherly in lighter conditions, stiff but a deep and rapid roller. Very long in staying and wearing. Stowed provisions badly, 4 months being maximum, with 93 tons water. Required considerable additional iron knees and fastenings later in her career, which further reduced the ballast and water she could stow.

Based on two undated reports, one in the late 1790s and the other about 1814.

Immortalité, 36 guns, Lorient 1795 [12pdr ship], P J Penetreau (captured 1798)

	Draught (ft-ins)		Freeboard (ft-ins)	Ballast (tons)			Victualled
	Fwd	aft	midships port	Iron	shingle	water	for
(1806)	16-8	18-2	6-2	85	160	63	3 months [CS]

A very stiff ship that would bear a press of sail 'better than most', but not particularly fast (11¾kts before the wind is the highest specific figure quoted); comparatively better large than close-hauled. Moderately weatherly, but seriously affected by a head sea because 'her bow is badly formed and at times she drops to leeward'. Uncommonly quick in wearing, but slow in stays, particularly under easy sail. Ballasting was sensitive, and stowage was poor – no more than 4 months' provisions and 63 tons of water was the most ever taken on board.

Based on report of 7 Apr 1806.

Loire, 40 guns, Nantes 1795, P Degay (captured 1798)

	Draught (ft-ins)		Freeboard (ft-ins)	Ballast (tons)			Victualled
	Fwd	aft	midships port	Iron	shingle	water	for
(1799)	16-7	17-6	7-5	90	85	83	4 months [CS]
(1814)	18-2	18-8	6-4	120	0	95	4 months [FS]

Fast off the wind (12½kts right before the wind), and close-hauled if water smooth (once touched 10½kts), but was leewardly and an extra false keel was recommended [one had been fitted already, in Mar 1801]. Comparatively far better sailing large than on a wind. Slack in stays and long in wearing. Stowed provisions poorly.

Based on reports of 6 Oct 1806 and 14 Jun 1814.

Niobe, 38 guns, ex-*Diane*, Toulon 1796, J N Sané (captured 1800)

	Draught (ft-ins)		Freeboard (ft-ins)	Ballast (tons)			Victualled
	Fwd	aft	midships port	Iron	shingle	water	for
(1814)	18-4	18-11	7-1	100	75	86	3 months [CS]

Generally regarded as a good, easy sea-boat and 'seldom outsailed or outcarried [in terms of sail set]'. At 10½kts close-hauled and 11½kts large, she seems to have been relatively better on a wind than off it. She was quite handy, but long in stays. Slightly more capacious than some French frigates, since she could manage 4½ months' provisions under hatches with 93 tons of water.

Based on reports of 15 Jun 1814 and 13 Mar 1816 (as a troopship with the spars of a 28-gun ship).

Desirée, 36 guns, Dunkirk 1796, ?designer (captured 1800)

	Draught (ft-ins)		Freeboard (ft-ins)	Ballast (tons)			Victualled
	Fwd	aft	midships port	Iron	shingle	water	for
(1812)	17-3	18-5	6-7	85	70	80	3 months [CS]
(1815)	18-2	18-5	5-10	85	20	?	?4 months [FS]

Moderately fast (9½kts close-hauled, 12kts large), particularly in a stiff breeze with a smooth sea, but 'not remarkably weatherly'. Deep, but easy in rolling and pitching, but very stiff. Generally handy, but long in stays if there was a head sea. Biggest problem was lack of stowage: in 1815 the captain complained that the breadroom could only hold 3 months' bread, and with foreign stores she was brought 12in deeper by the head than her optimum trim, 'which materially impedes her sailing'; the small quantity of ballast stowed made it impossible to land any in compensation for greater weight of stores.

Based on reports of 20 Jan 1812 and 30 Aug 1815.

Africaine, 38 guns, Rochefort 1798, R A Haran (captured 1801)

	Draught (ft-ins)		Freeboard (ft-ins)	Ballast (tons)			Victualled
	Fwd	aft	midships port	Iron	shingle	water	for
(1803)	17-8	18-11	6-3	142	48	120	6 months [FS]
(1807)	17-0	17-4	6-8	90	47	96	4 months [CS]

Fast, particularly off the wind (12-13kts large, 9kts close-hauled); leewardly in light winds, but better in stronger conditions. Similarly handy and responsive, except in lighter winds. Stiff, and a deep, quick but easy roller. Far more capacious than usual French frigates, able to stow 6 months' provisions under hatches and carry 120 tons of water.

Based on reports of 24 Feb 1803 and 26 Feb 1816.

Pique, 36 guns, ex-*Pallas*, St Malo 1800, ?designer (captured 1800)

	Draught (ft-ins)		Freeboard (ft-ins)	Ballast (tons)			Victualled
	Fwd	aft	midships port	Iron	shingle	water	for
(1802)	15-8	17-9	6-3	85	40	95	4 months [FS]
(1812)	16-2	17-8	7-0	85	35	80	3 months [CS]

Very fast close-hauled (10½kts), but less outstanding large (12kts), although one report gives 12½kts before the wind. The ship required additions to her rudder soon after entering British service to improve manoeuvrability; an addition to the false keel was also suggested to improve her windward performance, but in 1812 the captain could still opine: 'I think not so weatherly as the generality of English frigates but more than most French'. Quite handy, but occasionally complained of for slackness in stays and length of time taken in wearing. Stiff, and generally a good sea-boat, except in a head sea when she pitched heavily. Could stow 4 months' provisions well, except for bread (3 months in breadroom), and carry 95 tons of water; 5 months seems to have been the maximum stowage.

Based on reports of 21 Jul 1802, 22 Jan 1812, 14 Feb 1815, and 21 Dec 1818.

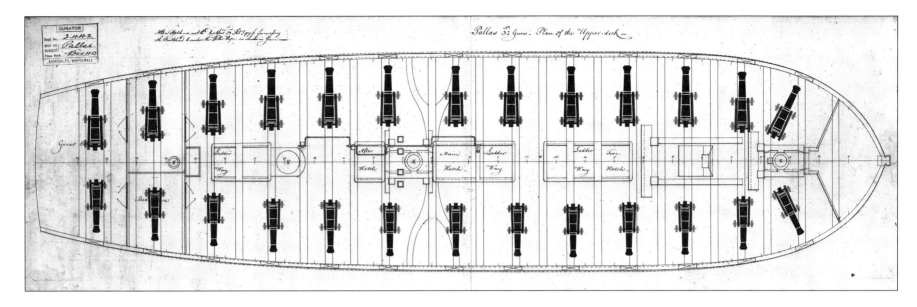

10. Armament

Pallas class 32, 1790, design upper deck draught.

This design deck plan has been overlaid with the outline of 9ft (top) and 8ft 18pdr guns in the housed position to show the cramped nature of the gundeck when carrying the larger weapon. Of course, weight was also a consideration, but space alone was sufficient cause for the development of a shorter main armament gun. On an unrelated but interesting issue, a note on the draught refers to a sketch sent to Deptford on 23 February 1796 to recess the bulkhead of the captain's quarters 'to enclose the tiller ropes'.

When the 12pdr frigate was introduced in 1756 no particular attention was given to its specific requirements regarding armament, but experience was to show that a shorter and lighter main deck gun was necessary.[117] History was repeated with the 18pdr frigate, improvement coming from the same triangular process of sea officer's complaint, Admiralty enquiry of Navy and Ordnance Boards, and a recommended solution.

The first 38s and 36s went to sea with the only 18pdr on the establishment, a 9ft weapon with a median weight of 41cwt. With only twenty-six on the main deck the 36s could carry the weight without complaint, but the 38s were overburdened. After only a few months' experience with his new command Captain Pearson of the *Arethusa* queried the weight of the guns in November 1781, but was told that this was the only gun available and – the Navy Board's most common defence – nobody else had raised the issue: 'on the contrary, the best of characters' was enjoyed by the class, whereas in fact only *Minerva* and *Latona* had been completed and the latter was already showing signs of uneasiness caused by carrying so much weight a long way forward and aft.

Pearson would not give up, and since he enjoyed the favour of the Admiralty following his gallantry during the *Serapis*–*Bonhomme Richard* action, his views had to be considered. The Navy Board believed the 38s 'very well able to support common guns of 18pdrs from which weight we apprehend no danger to the ship', but the issue was really one of sailing performance and the Board conceded that if lighter guns of equal power could be devised then it would be an improvement. The decision was taken in June 1782 to cast two experimental short guns, which were completed by 10 June, and a trial was carried out on 6 July in the presence of two naval officers, including Captain Fielding of the

Minerva. As a result of successful test firings, the 8ft 38cwt gun became the establishment weapon for 38-gun frigates. It was somewhat ironic that the smaller 36s, which continued to carry the 9ft gun, were actually equipped with a more powerful weapon.[118]

When the 18pdr 32-gun class came into service in 1793 the ships were given the longer gun, presumably because the 8ft weapon was specifically established for 38s only. However, they were somewhat cramped and lively sea-boats and the captain of the *Pallas* found the guns unmanageable in a press of wind. On investigation it transpired that the 9ft guns were of a new cast that averaged 2½cwt more than those of 1782 and in Nov 1794 the ship was supplied with guns of the old model.[119] However, the complaints continued and in February 1795 the Navy Board was instructed to send a list of 18pdr frigates to the Ordnance with a view to replacing their upper deck guns with lighter weapons as opportunity arose.[120] As a result in June 1796 the short 8ft gun was issued to *Unicorn*, followed by *Stag* in September and *Pallas* herself in August 1797.[121] The next class were also affected and were eventually converted to the shorter weapon as their captains requested, the *Alcmene*, for example, being issued with the new guns in August 1797. Later 32s were issued with the 8ft gun from commissioning, but concern over the weight problems may have contributed to the decision to arm the fir-built *Maidstone* and *Shannon* with 12pdrs, since the lighter and consequently more heavily ballasted softwood ships were prone to deep rolling, which was bound to exacerbate the problems of handling heavy guns. It is worth noting that from the 1790s long guns were

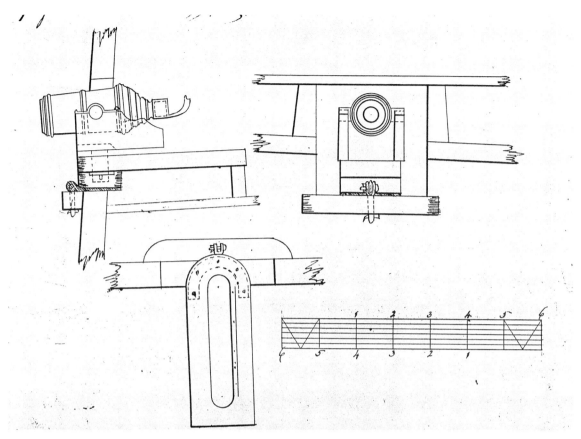

Carronade mounting, dated 12 December 1781.

This drawing from the Deptford Dockyard records accompanies a note from the Navy Board saying it is the 'mode of fixing the carronades on board His Majesty's Ship *Artois* with a copy of a letter from Capt Macbride ... for your Information and Guidance in fixing them.' The early shape of the gun with its monkey-tail tiller (cut off in the drawing?) is noteworthy, as is the mounting. Macbride and the *Artois* played a large part in the development of the carronade, progressing from these 18pdrs to 68pdrs before the American War was over. *(PRO Adm 106/3472)*

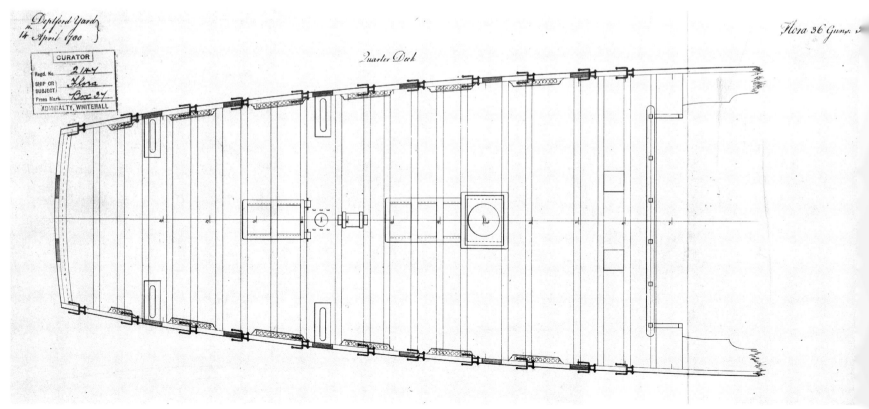

generally cast somewhat heavier than earlier models, the new Blomefield pattern having more metal around the breech; this was necessary to withstand the power of the new 'cylinder' gunpowder formally adopted on 6 October 1795.

Officially, this left only the 36s with the 9ft gun but there were always exceptions to the establishment occasioned by specific requests. The *Melampus* requested short guns in November 1798 (the difference in weight was now nearly 5cwt per gun); even the *Euryalus*, a new 36, received 8ft guns in June 1803, while conversely the *Naiad*, 38, was given 9ft 18pdrs on application from her captain in May 1797. Furthermore, some large ex-French 38s like *Uranie* were initially fitted with the longer gun, as were some of the later British 38s. Whether by intention or oversight the longer gun continued to be issued, so that on 21 April 1808 the *Unicorn* had again to have shorter guns substituted.

SECONDARY ARMAMENT 1778-1800

The 18pdr frigates were to be major beneficiaries of the carronade revolution, but the armament on their upperworks was increased even before the first of them went to sea. Captain Fielding, appointed to *Minerva* while she was building, suggested that the proposed establishment left the ship both under-armed and weakly manned. On consideration the Navy Board felt that the 18pdr ships were built strongly enough for 9pdrs to replace 6pdrs on the quarterdeck and forecastle and increased the complements to 280, with 270 for 36s; they were also allowed another lieutenant.[122] The Navy Board had suggested

a a pair of 12pdr chase guns, but the addition of a third calibre seemed likely to produce confusion in action and eventually a longer 9pdr was deemed sufficient (7ft 6in 24½cwt, instead of the quarterdeck 7ft 23½cwt models). The *Dimensions Book* for 1794-97 shows the 12pdr chase guns on these classes, but it is unlikely any were shipped; in all known cases the chase guns were 9pdrs.

However, it was the long march of the carronade along the upperworks of British warships that was to be the most radical improvement in armament during the last two decades of the eighteenth century. The rapid evolution of the carronade was the product of a desperate strategic situation in which the Royal Navy was significantly outnumbered and the Navy Board sought to offset the quantitive inferiority with two 'secret weapons'. The first was coppering, which endowed the fleet with unprecedented mobility, and the second was the carronade which was to give individual ships superiority in action, even against opponents of nominally greater force. In the close actions of the 1790s the big carronades became ship-smashing weapons but it is clear that they were originally narrower in conception. In 1779 parallel experiments were going on with coehorns (small shell-firing mortars) for use in the tops as well as multi-barrel small arms, and the early carronade experiments stress their value against personnel and top-hamper. Middleton, the Comptroller and driving force of the Navy Board, was anxious to give British ships a weapon which could allow them to chose action if they desired – by destroying the enemy's rigging – and a counter to the supposed French advantage in boarding (rate for rate, they usually carried larger crews). This was particularly significant for cruisers which often operated alone, so naturally frigates received much of the initial attention.

After successful experiments with 12pdr and 18pdr carronades an Establishment was promulgated in July 1779, which gave 38s six and four 18pdrs for quarterdeck and forecastle respectively, with four and four 18s for the 36s. This did not take account of the variety of forecastle and quarterdeck layouts and was generally too ambitious as to the number that could be fitted without threatening the shrouds, so in January 1780 the fixed establishment was cancelled to await more experience. The exact number of carronades taken to sea by particular frigates is therefore difficult to ascertain. Based on her logs, *Flora* originally shipped eight as per establishment, but took only six in

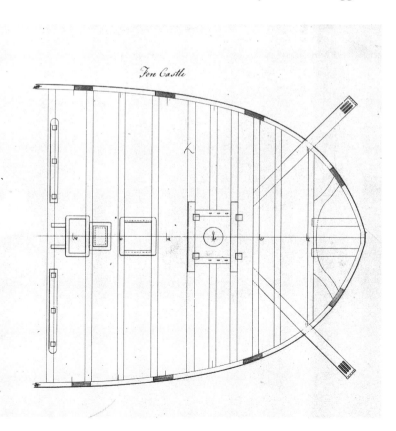

Flora, 36 guns, design quarterdeck draught with fitting out details, dated Deptford, 14 April 1780.

As the first 18pdr ship to enter service, and the first to carry carronades from the outset, it was natural that *Flora* would be used to work out the novel details of their fitting. As a result both the sheer & profile and quarterdeck draughts are unusually finely detailed. The original system of carronade supply was very cumbersome in that the foundry supplied the guns but the Dockyards made the carriages, hence the need to depict the slides on the deck plan. It also shows the shot garlands (soon to be moved to the hatch coamings) and the hammock cranes. An elevation of *Flora*'s quarterdeck barricades is preserved in the Deptford Dockyard records, and was reproduced by Brian Lavery in *The Arming and Fitting of English Ships of War*, p247.

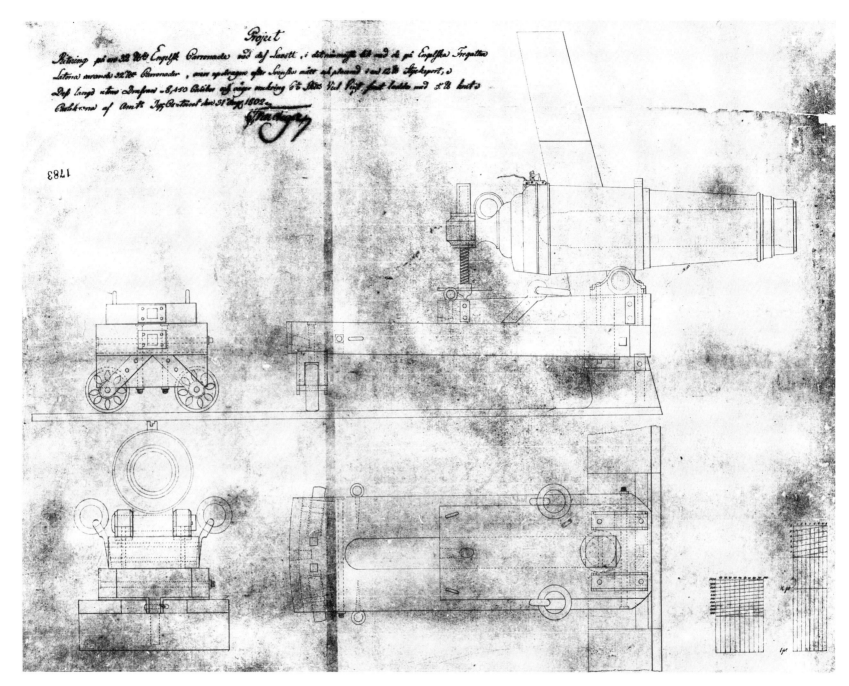

English 32pdr carronade, from the frigate *Latona*, dated 31 Aug 1802.

Official Admiralty drawings of guns are very rare, and they usually depict the odd or experimental weapons that depart from the norm. This Swedish drawing, indicative of Continental interest in this predominantly English phenomenon, is known to be a standard weapon from a specific ship. Compared with the 1781 weapon, points to note include: the fitting on the 'outside principle', allowing the gun to be run out far enough to protect the shrouds; the 'nozzle' extension of the muzzle, for much the same purpose; screw elevating gear; and wheels to make traversing easy. There is also a gunlock, which was in widespread use in the Royal Navy by this time.
(Krigsarkivet, Stockholm)

October 1781, finishing the war with four on the quarterdeck only. [123] In 1782 *Perseverance* carried only two 18pdrs on the quarterdeck, while the 38s in commission all had four 18pdrs on the quarterdeck but *Arethusa* also had two on the forecastle.

The Navy Board clearly had a vision of these guns dismantling top-hamper and wanted langridge and case shot issued. At their prompting an elaborate trial against a target simulating rigging was carried out. It was reported in September 1780 that langridge and case were largely useless, being too small, but that grape with individual shot of not less than 1lb weight was effective at 1000-1200yds, particularly when using

The *Leda* class 38 HMS *Shannon*, contemporary model.

The US Naval Academy model of the *Shannon* depicts a frigate of the time as actually fitted for service, although some details, most notably the boats, are not represented. The carronades are well modelled and correct in number but the pairs of 9pdr chase guns that should be on the forecastle and quarterdeck are missing; at least two of the forecastle carronades would have been carried on the quarterdeck. Note the effect of the hammocks stowed along the tops of the barricades and in the waist. *(US Naval Academy Museum)*

reduced, one-third charges. The Navy Board also sponsored the development of larger calibres, enthusiastically taking up the Carron Company's August 1780 offer of a gun to fire 68pdr solid shot (or a 56pdr shell). Two were ordered for the forecastle of the French prize *Artois* in Oct 1781 and by January 1782 two big carronades were ordered to be supplied to any large vessel on request; of 68pdr, 42pdr or 32pdr calibre, they were to be an addition to the force of the ship, and fitted on the forecastle 'to annoy the rigging and sails of the enemy at the beginning of an action'.[124]

There were significant problems with the early carronades and their mountings, not least the blast effect from their short muzzles on their own ship's shrouds. In December 1781, Captain Macbride of the *Artois*, an early convert to the cause, advocated casting the guns longer by a calibre or two, but this was not done in a systematic way until the 1790s. In March 1783 carronades were ordered removed from ships in peacetime commission to save unnecessary stress on their hulls, and in June 1786 the quarterdeck solid barricading was likewise prohibited. Carronade development came to a halt.

On the outbreak of war there was no Establishment in force and captains requested whatever they thought most appropriate. William Dillon, for example, records that his captain in the *Thetis* refused to take any because the establishment allowed no extra men to fight them; he also suggests that the extra weight was an impediment to speed.[125] However, when carronades were wanted the Board of Ordnance proved less than co-operative, meeting a request for 32pdrs in July 1793 with the petulant claim that the calibre was not on the old establishment and they had just placed contracts for sufficient carronades of other sorts.[126] However, this began the process of considering a new Establishment. The Ordnance still felt that the concept of the carronade was relatively untried, and was also bothered about the effect of blast on the rigging, not to mention the cost of replacing many otherwise unusable 6pdr and 9pdr long guns. As a result a compromise was reached with the Navy Board in October 1794 in which carronades were added to upperworks, but not 'in the wake of the rigging'.

This new Establishment also included weapons of much improved design and fitting. For a while in 1794 captains' requests specify 'long' carronades with screw elevating gear and traversing slide mountings.[127] Detailed modifications continued to be made but it seems that by this date the main features of the 'mature' carronade were already in place – the elongated nozzle, the underside lug instead of trunnions, and the familiar slide of what came to be called 'the inside principle'. Unfortunately, there was a considerable demand for the new 32pdr and in August 1795 the Ordnance Board admitted that they could not be cast quickly enough, and were instructed by the Admiralty to give priority to the new brigs (which were not designed for long guns), but frigates were to come next.[128]

Despite shortages and interim fitting the carronade began to take over most of the ports on frigates' upperworks. More and more captains tried to exchange their rather feeble long guns for powerful carronades and in May 1799 the Navy Board petitioned the Admiralty to change the Establishment to retain only pairs of long guns on the quarterdeck and on the forecastle as chase guns. However, the carronades were to be fitted on the outside principle and were to be allowed initially only to new ships fitting out;[129] needless to say, by the end of the year it had come to be accepted that the Establishment would apply to all ships as they refitted.

There was a tendency to replace even the two quarterdeck long guns

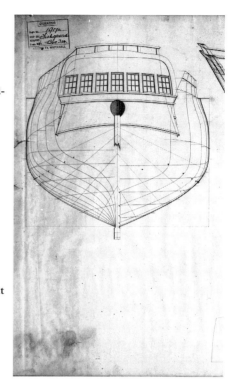

Fisgard, 38 guns, ex-French *Résistance*, as fitted sheer & profile draught, dated Plymouth, August 1798.

In earlier periods the British were often criticised for overloading their own ships with guns, and extending the practice to foreign prizes, by increasing the calibre of their main armament. However, in the French Revolutionary War the opposite was often the case. The *Fisgard* is a prime example, mounting upper deck 24pdrs when captured, but carrying only 18pdrs in Royal Navy service. Although a very large frigate at 1182 tons, the ship had a reputation for being structurally weak, and it must have been clear that heavy weight of metal would exacerbate the problem, given the harsher conditions of employment for British cruisers.

with carronades (chauvinists undoubtedly believed British warships had no need of stern chasers), but this does not seem to have received official sanction until December 1804.[130] There was a short-lived return to a mixture of long guns and carronades for some ships in 1803-6, but this was due to a misguided decision to adopt Bentham's non-recoil mountings. The full details of this development properly belong to a later volume, but in outline, experiments were conducted from August 1803, a decision was made in October 1804 to fit only non-recoil mountings to frigates in future, and the order was rescinded in July 1806.[131] The mountings were fitted on the inside principle and pivoted to allow reloading without exposing the gun crew outside the barricade; the muzzle was therefore inside the port, which threatened the shrouds with blast damage. This is the reason for the return to long guns 'in the wake of the rigging', although it was also possible to fit recoiling carronades on the outside principle in those positions.[132]

COMPLEMENT

The crews of 38s and 36s were originally established as 280 and 260 respectively, and these totals were restored after the reduced peacetime establishment on the outbreak of war in February 1793. The first 18pdr 32s were originally to have had 220 men but the Navy Board recommended the same as 36s.[133] The numbers were reduced as part of the reorganisation associated with the carronade establishment of 19 November 1794 – to 274, 254 and 244. This was obviously unsatisfactory and many successful applications from captains for more men led the Admiralty to reconsider. After consulting the Navy Board, an extra 10 men were added to each establishment by order of 1 June 1796.

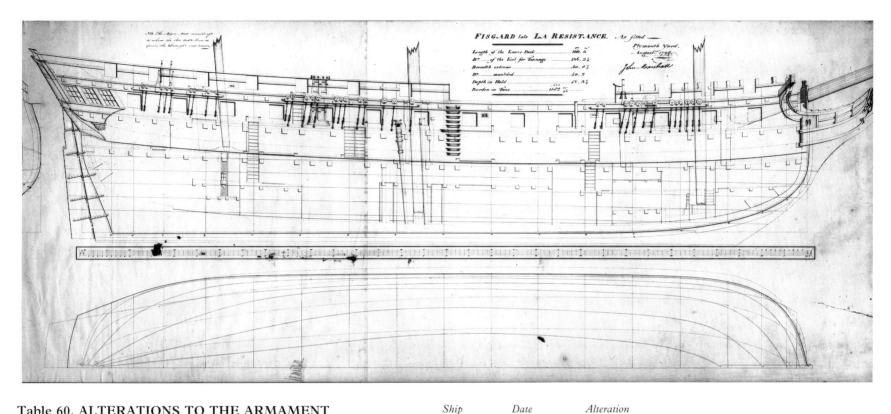

FISGARD late LA RESISTANCE. As fitted — Plymouth Yard. August 1796. John Marshall

Length of the Lower Deck.....
D° of the Keil for Tonnage.....
Breadth extreme.....
D° moulded.....
Depth in Hold.....
Burden in Tons.....

Table 60. ALTERATIONS TO THE ARMAMENT ESTABLISHMENTS OF BRITISH 18pdr FRIGATES OF THE 1778-1801 PERIOD

Note: Carronades were ordered removed from ships in commission in March 1783 and there was no establishment of carronades in force in 1793. The Oct 1794 Establishment added the following carronades to 18pdr ships:

38s and 36s   6 x 32pdrs QD; 2 x 32pdrs FC
32s   4 x 24pdrs QD; 2 x 24pdrs FC

By Admiralty Order of 4 June 1799 all frigates in future were to have carronades for all QD & FC ports except 2 long chase guns on each deck; carronades to be on the 'outside principle' and fitted as ships came forward for service.

Ship	Date	Alteration
***Minerva* class, 38s**		
Establishment:		28 x 18s; 8 x 9s; 2 x 9s
Minerva	[was in the E Indies on the outbreak of war]	
	13 Jul 1795	Establishment
	28 Feb 1798	16 x 9 UD; 4 x 9 QD [troopship]
	15 Sep 1806	Carr on outside principle replace guns and non-recoil carr
Arethusa	19 Oct 1793	14 x 32 carr replace 10 x 9s
	11 Jan 1794	2 x 9s added on FC
	6 May 1805	8 x 32 carr; 2 x 32 carr, 2 x 9s
	4 Jul 1805	6 x 9s, 6 x 32 carr; 4 x 9s, 2 x 32 carr
	14 Sep 1808	9s replaced with 32 carr
Phaeton	29 Jan 1793	2 carr (calibre unknown) added
	13 Jun 1794	Establishment
	6 Apr 1795	Establishment

Ship	Date	Alteration
	12 Jul 1803	Establishment
	23 Sep 1822	14 x 32 carr; 2 x 9s, 2 x 32 carr [*]
Thetis	18 Feb 1793	Establishment
	16 Oct 1793	2 x 42 carr replace foremost 2 x 18 on UD; 6 x 32 carr added on QD & FC
	19 Jan 1800	16 x 9s UD; 4 x 6s [troopship]
	17 Apr 1805	28 x 18s; 14 x 32 carr; 2 x 9s, 2 x 32 carr
	2 Jul 1805	8 x 9s, 6 x 32 carr; 2 x 9s, 2 x 32 carr
	22 Feb 1808	6 x 9s replaced by 6 x 32 carr
***Latona*, 38**		
Establishment:		28 x 18s; 8 x 9s; 2 x 9s
Latona	8 Apr 1793	Establishment
	6 Apr 1795	Establishment
	13 Mar 1800	Carr fitted as new Establishment
	23 Jun 1806	Carr on inside principle instead of long guns at present onboard.
***Flora* class, 36s**		
Establishment:		26 x 18s; 8 x 9s; 2 x 9s
Flora	29 Apr 1797	To have 1794 Establishment carr
	6 May 1805	8 x 32 carr; 2 x 9s, 2 x 32 carr
Thalia	4 Feb 1793	4 x 32 carr added
	11 Apr 1794	2 x 18 carr added
	14 Dec 1796	Establishment
	15 Apr 1805	6 x 32 carr; 2 x 9s, 2 x 32 carr
	12 Apr ?	4 x 32 carr added
Crescent	7 Feb 1793	QD 9s replaced with 18s carr
	24 Apr 1799	10 x 32 carr, 2 x 9s
	26 Sep 1808	2 x 9s on QD replaced by 2 x 32 carr
Romulus	22 Jan 1793	Establishment

Ship	Date	Alteration
	20 Jun 1799	Establishment
	26 Mar 1803	24 x 18s UD; 8 x 18 carr [harbour service]

Perseverance class, 36s

Ship	Date	Alteration
Establishment:		26 x 18s; 8 x 9s; 2 x 9s
Perseverance [was in the E Indies on the outbreak of war]		
	9 Jul 1793	Laid up [became prison hulk]
Phoenix	[was in the E Indies on the outbreak of war]	
	13 Jul 1793	Establishment
	31 Dec 1795	Establishment
	26 Apr 1803	Establishment
	1 Jan 1813	12 x 32 carr; 2 x 9s, 2 x 32 carr [★]
Inconstant	8 Jan 1793	Establishment
	7 Mar 1797	10 x 9s UD; 4 x 6s QD [troopship]
	20 Mar 1800	supplied with 24 carr
	25 Oct 1803	10 x 9s UD; 4 x 6s QD [troopship]
	4 Dec 1805	26 x 12s UD; 2 x 6s, 6 x 24 carr; 2 x 6, 2 x 24 carr
	21 Jun 1809	26 x 18s; 12 x 32 carr; 2 x 9s, 2 x 32 carr
Leda	9 Jan 1793	Establishment
	15 Apr 1795	Establishment

Melampus, 36

Ship	Date	Alteration
Establishment:		26 x 18s; 8 x 9s; 2 x 9s
Melampus	10 Apr 1793	Establishment
	25 Jun 1793	6 x 32 carr replace 6 x 18 carr
	6 Jul 1793	32 carr replace QD 9s
	12 Dec 1799	6 x 32 carr replace 6 x 9s on QD
	2 Oct 1804	6 x 32 carr supplied

Beaulieu, 40

Ship	Date	Alteration
Establishment:		28 x 18s; 8 x 9s; 4 x 9s
	20 Feb 1793	2 x 32 carr, 6 x 18 carr added
	29 Dec 179	6 new model carr replace old ones

Pallas class, 32s

Ship	Date	Alteration
Establishment:		26 x 18s; 4 x 6s; 2 x 6s
Pallas	22 Jan 1793	Establishment
Stag	26 Jul 1794	4 x 32 carr added to QD
	31 Jul 1794	2 x 32 carr added to FC
	2 Mar 1798	new 'long' 24 carr replace 32 carr
Unicorn	26 Aug 1794	4 x 32s carr; 2 x 32s carr added

Alcmene class, 32s

Ship	Date	Alteration
Establishment:		26 x 18s; 4 x 6s; 2 x 6s
Galatea	27 Jun 1794	8 x 18 carr added
Cerberus	7 Nov 1794	4 x 24 carr; 2 x 24 carr added
	3 Jan 1799	6 x 24 carr replace 4 x 6s
Lively	28 Oct 1794	Establishment
	?27 Aug 1795	4 x 32 carr added [DB]
Alcmene	21 Mar 1795	Establishment

Artois class, 38s

Ship	Date	Alteration
Establishment (7 Dec 1793):		28 x 18s; 8 x 9s; 2 x 9s
Artois	29 Mar 1794	4 x 32 carr added
	9 May 1794	2 x 9s replace 2 x 32 carr
Diana	26 Apr 1794	2 x 24 carr added to FC
	14 May 1794	4 x 24 carr added to QD

Ship	Date	Alteration
	9 Apr 1806	32 carr for QD in lieu of 9s
	Jan 1812	14 x 32 carr; 4 x 32 carr [★]
Diamond	3 Mar 1794	Establishment
	26 Mar 1796	'supplied with 5½in shells for 24pdr guns'
	21 Dec 1798	Establishment
	15 Jun 1806	Carr to remain in wake of rigging
Apollo	8 Jul 1794	Establishment
	24 Sep 1798	Establishment
Jason	21 Jun 1794	4 x 18 carr added to QD
	6 Apr 1795	4 x 32 carr; 2 x 32 carr in lieu of 18 carr
Seahorse	1 Aug 1794	4 x 24 carr; 2 x 24 carr added
	29 Oct 1796	32 carr replace 24 carr on QD & FC
	18 Oct 1797	Light 18s to replace heavy ones on UD
	13 Mar 1800	Carr fitted as new Establishment
	12 Sep 1815	14 x 32 carr; 2 x 9s, 2 x 32 carr [★]
Clyde	8 Sep 1795	8 x 9s, 6 x 32 carr; 2 x 9s, 2 x 32 carr
Tamer	8 Sep 1795	8 x 9s, 6 x 32 carr; 2 x 9s, 2 x 32 carr
Ethalion	9 May 1797	8 x 9s, 6 x 32 carr; 2 x 9s, 2 x 32 carr
Clyde (ii)	28 Jan 1808	Carr slides altered [non-recoil?]
	7 May 1810	Carr fitted on recoil principle

Phoebe class 36s

Ship	Date	Alteration
Establishment (16 Mar 1795):		26 x 18s; 8 x 9s, 6 x 32 carr; 2 x 9s, 2 x 32 carr
Dryad	11 Mar 1795	Establishment
	4 Mar 1798	4 x 32 carr replace 4 x 9s
	Jun 1829	12 x 32 carr; 2 x 9s, 2 x 32 carr [★]
Caroline	16 Mar 1795	Establishment
	4 Mar 1805	2 x 6s supplied
Doris	11 Mar 1795	Establishment
Phoebe	16 Mar 1795	Establishment
	25 Jan 1813	2 x 9s, 12 x 32 carr; 2 x 9s, 2 x 32 carr [★]
	28 Aug 1815	26 x 18s (short) UD; 12 x 32 carr; 4 x 9s, 2 x 32 carr [★]
Fortunee	27 Nov 1800	Establishment
	30 Nov 1811	Light 18s UD; 32 carr replaced by 24 carr
	20 Jan 1812	26 x 18 (light) UD; 12 x 24; 2 x 9s, 2 x 24 carr [★]
	20 Feb 1813	26 x 18 (8ft) UD; 2 x 12s (brass), 12 x 24 carr; 2 x 12s (brass), 2 x 24 carr [★]

Amazon class 36s

Ship	Date	Alteration
Establishment (16 Mar 1794):		26 x 18s; 8 x 9s, 6 x 32 carr; 2 x 9s, 2 x 32 carr
Amazon	16 Mar 1794	Establishment
Emerald	16 Mar 1794	Establishment
	22 May 1806	6 x 9s, 6 x 32 carr; 2 x 9s, 2 x 32 carr
	15 Jun 1806	All 32 carr on recoil principle plus 2 x 9s
Trent	8 Sep 1795	Establishment but 2 x 12s not 9s on FC
	5 Nov 1800	All 32 carr on QD & FC
Glenmore	8 Sep 1795	Establishment but 2 x 12s not 9s on FC
	20 Feb 1800	32 carr to replace all except 2 x 9s

Sirius, 36

Ship	Date	Alteration
Establishment (15 Feb 1796):		26 x 18s; 6 x 9s; 2 x 9s
Sirius	24 Mar 1800	6 x 32 carr replace 9s on QD

Ship	Date	Alteration
Naiad, 38		
Establishment (14 Nov 1795):		28 x 18s; 8 x 9s; 2 x 9s
Naiad	9 May 1797	8 x 9s, 6 x 32 carr; 2 x 9s, 2 x 32 carr
	1 Feb 1812	2 x 9s, 10 x 32 carr; 2 x 9s, 4 x 32 carr [*]
Boadicea, 38		
Establishment (14 Nov 1795):		28 x 18s; 8 x 9s; 2 x 9s
Boadicea	9 May 1797	8 x 9s, 6 x 32 carr; 2 x 9s, 2 x 32 carr
	1 Jun 1799	32 carr replace all but 2 QD & FC 9s
	Aug 1827	14 x 32 carr; 2 x 9s, 2 x 32 carr [*]
Hydra, 38		
Establishment (14 Nov 1795):		28 x 18s; 8 x 9s; 2 x 9s
Hydra	20 Apr 1796	Establishment
	19 Jan 1801	Establishment
	20 Sep 1813	12 x 32 carr UD; 4 x 32 carr QD; 1 x 12 FC as troopship [*]
Active, 38		
Establishment (6 May 1797):		28 x 18s; 8 x 9s, 6 x 32 carr; 2 x 9s, 2 x 32 carr
Active	30 Jan 1800	14 x 32 carr QD & FC [plus 4 x 9s chase]
Amazon class, 38s		
Establishment (16 Apr 1797):		28 x 18s; 8 x 9s, 6 x 32s carr; 2 x 9s, 2 x 32 carr
Amazon	6 Jun 1799	12 x 32 carr, 2 x 9s QD
	2 Jul 1799	2 x 32 carr, 2 x 9s FC added
	31 Dec 1811	2 x 9s, 12 x 32 carr; 2 x 9s, 2 x 32 carr, 2 x 18 carr (boat guns?) [*]
Hussar	6 May 1797	As Establishment
Leda class, 38s		
Establishment (6 May 1797):		28 x 18s; 8 x 9s, 6 x 32 carr; 2 x 9s, 2 x 32 carr
Leda	30 Dec 1799	14 x 32 carr for QD
Pomone	26 Apr 1803	Establishment
	20 Oct 1804	14 x 32 carr; 2 x 9s, 2 x 32 carr
Shannon	12 Jun 1804	2 x 9s, 12 x 32 carr; 2 x 9s, 2 x 32 carr
Amphion class, 32s		
Establishment (16 Dec 1796):		26 x 18s; 4 x 6s, 4 x 24 carr; 2 x 6s, 2 x 24 carr
Amphion	31 Oct 1804	24 carr replace 6s
	10 Nov 1804	Carr fitted on non-recoil principle
	1 Jan 1817	10 x 24 carr; 2 x 9s, 4 x 24 carr [*]
Establishment (Feb 1800)		26 x 18s; 2 x 6s, 8 x 24 carr; 2 x 6s, 2 x 24 carr
Medusa	Feb 1800	Establishment
Aeolus	1 Jan 1809	2 x 9s, 8 x 24 carr; 4 x 9s [*]
Nereus	1 Jan 1813	2 x 9s, 8 x 24 carr; 2 x 9s, 2 x 24 carr
Penelope class, 36s		
Establishment (22 Aug 1798):		26 x 18s; 6 x 6s; 6 x 32 carr; 4 x 6s, 2 x 32 carr
Penelope	30 Oct 1798	9s replace 6s in new class Establishment
Amethyst	13 May 1799	32 carr replace all but 2 QD & FC 9s
Jason	20 Feb 1798	6 x 9s, 6 x 32 carr; 4 x 9s, 2 x 32 carr
	30 Jan 1800	14 x 32 carr for QD & FC [plus 4 x 9s chase]

Ship	Date	Alteration
Narcissus class, 32s		
Establishment:		26 x 18s; 4 x 6s, 6 x 24 carr; 2 x 6s, 2 x 24 carr
Narcissus	11 Jun 1800	26 x 24s Gover pattern on UD
	24 Jun 1800	2 x 9s, 8 x 24 carr QD
	24 Jul 1801	26 x 18s on UD
	14 Jan 1812	26 x 24s Gover UD; 2 x 9s, 8 x 24 carr; 2 x 9s, 2 x 24 carr [*]
Apollo class, 36s		
Establishment (20 Feb 1799):		26 x 18s; 8 x 9s, 4 x 32 carr; 2 x 9s, 4 x 32 carr
Apollo	17 June 1799	2 x 9s, 10 x 32 carr; 4 x 32 carr, 2 x 9s
Blanche	15 Dec 1800	Establishment
Euryalus	16 Jun 1803	2 x 9s, 10 x 32 carr; 4 x 32 carr, 2 x 9s
	29 Nov 1804	Short 18s replace long model on UD
Aigle class, 36s		
Establishment (20 Feb 1799):		26 x 18s; 4 x 9s, 8 x 32 carr; 4 x 9s, 2 x 32 carr
Aigle	30 Jan 1800	14 x 32 carr QD & FC [plus 4 x 9s chase]
	15 Oct 1801	4 x 9s, 8 x 32 carr; 4 x 9s, 2 x 32 carr
Ethalion, 36		
Establishment (7 Sep 1799)		26 x 18s; 14 x 32 carr; 2 x 9s, 4 x 32 carr
Ethalion (25 Nov 1802):		Establishment
Lively class, 38s		
Establishment (12 Jun 1804)		28 x 18s; 2 x 9s, 12 x 32 carr; 2 x 9s, 2 x 32 carr
Lively	?12 Jun 1804:	Establishment

Table 61. ALTERATIONS TO THE ARMAMENT ESTABLISHMENTS OF 18pdr PRIZE FRIGATES CAPTURED UP TO 1801

Ship	Date	Alteration
Armed with 26 x 18pdrs on upper deck		
Modeste	15 Aug 1797	8 x 9s, 2 x 9s
San Fiorenzo	30 Mar 1795	6 x 9s, 6 x 32 carr; 2 x 9s, 2 x 32 carr
	21 Mar 1809	12 x 32 carr; 2 x 9s, 9 x 32 carr
	25 May 1810	14 x 9s UD; 6 x 18 carr QD; 2 x 6s [troopship]
Immortalité	5 Dec 1798	8 x 9s, 4 x 24 carr; 2 x 9s, 2 x 24 carr
Princess Charlotte	2 Apr 1801	2 x 9s, 12 x 32 carr; 2 x 9s, 4 x 32 carr
Pique	22 Apr 1800	2 x 9s, 10 x 24 carr; 4 x 9s, 2 x 24 carr
	28 Jul 1800	4 x 9s, 14 x 32 carr on QD/FC
	28 Aug 1811	2 x 9s, 10 x 32 carr; 2 x 9s, 4 x 32 carr
	5 Mar 1813	2 x 32 carr added in foremost QD ports
Desirée	12 Aug 1800	2 x 9s, 8 x 32 carr; 2 x 9s, 2 x 32 carr
	26 Sep 1800	2 x 9s, 12 x 32 carr; 2 x 9s, 2 x 32 carr
	4 Nov 1800	2 extra 32 carr
	4 Dec 1800	2 extra 32 carr [repeat of above?]
Armed with 28 x 18pdrs on upper deck		
Hebe	15 Nov 1793	Establishment
	7 Mar 1797	16 x 9s UD; 4 x 6s QD & FC [troopship]
[*Blonde*]	31 Dec 1805	28 x 18s UD; 8 x 9s, 6 x 32 carr; 4 x 9s, 2 x 32 carr
Perle [renamed *Amethyst*]		8 x 6s, 6 x 32 carr; 2 x 6s, 2 x 32 carr
Aréthuse [later *Undaunted*]	29 Nov 1794	6 x 6s, 4 x 24 carr; 4 x 6s
Impérieuse	30 Mar 1798	8 x 9s, 6 x 32 carr; 2 x 9s, 2 x 32 carr
	6 Oct 1795	8 x 32 carr for spare ports
	3 Dec 1795	18 carr to replace 12 carr for launch
[*Unité*]	17 Dec 1804	12 x 32 carr; 2 x 9s, 2 x 32 carr (26 x 18s on UD)
	9 Jul 1805	6 x 9s, 6 x 32 carr; 4 x 9s, 2 x 32 carr
Sybille	8 Dec 1794	12 x 9s; 4 x 9s
	20 Mar 1795	2 x 32 carr added to QD
	24 Apr 1795	2 carr added [additional to above?]
	17 Dec 1804	12 x 32 carr; 4 x 9s, 2 x 32 carr
	5 Jul 1805	8 x 9s, 6 x 32 carr; 4 x 9s, 2 x 32 carr
	5 Dec 1807	FC 2 x 9s, otherwise all carr on outside recoil principle on QD/FC
Melpomène	30 Mar 1795	8 x 9s, 6 x 32 carr; 2 x 9s, 2 x 32 carr
	2 Oct 1795	supplied with carr intended for *Undaunted* [ex-*Aréthuse*]
	3 Feb 1808	UD 9ft 18s replaced by 8ft model
Révolutionnaire	19 Jan 1795	8 x 9s, 6 x 32 carr; 2 x 9s, 2 x 32 carr
	13 Mar 1803	UD long 18s replaced by 32 carr
	31 Oct 1812	28 x 18s UD; 14 x 32 carr; 2 x 9s, 2 x 32 carr
Minerve	15 Jun 1798	32 carr on QD/FC with long 9s in wake of the rigging
Virginie	25 Jun 1796	8 x 9s, 4 x 24 carr; 2 x 9s, 2 x 24 carr
	17 Dec 1804	8 x 32 carr; 2 x 9s, 2 x 32 carr
	18 May 1805	12 x 32 carr; 2 x 9s, 2 x 32 carr
Amelia	21 Jul 1796	8 x 9s, 4 x 24 carr; 2 x 9s, 2 x 24 carr
	6 Sep 1797	10 x 32 carr in lieu of 24s
	30 Oct 1797	2 long 9s replace 2 short 9s
	12 Oct 1807	14 x 32 carr; 2 x 9s, 4 x 32 carr
	18 Sep 1810	2 x 9s for FC
Tartu	1 Apr 1797	8 x 9s, 4 x 24 carr; 2 x 9s, 2 x 24 carr
[*Uranie*]	2 Oct 1799	8 x 32 carr replace 8 x 9s
	1 Apr 1804	UD 28 x 18s replaced by 26 x 12s
Fisgard	9 May 1797	8 x 9s, 6 x 32 carr; 2 x 9s, 2 x 32 carr
Loire	31 Dec 1798	8 x 9s, 4 x 24 carr; 4 x 9s, 2 x 24 carr
	4 May 1799	32 carr to replace equal no of 24 carr
	16 Jun 1800	2 x 9s on Schank's carriages
	12 Oct 1807	14 x 32 carr; 2 x 9s, 4 x 32 carr
Diane	28 Feb 1800	2 x 9s, 10 x 32 carr; 2 x 9s, 2 x 32 carr
[*Niobe*]	6 Feb 1813	2 x 9s on FC exchanged for 2 x 32 carr
	7 Jun 1814	No weapons on FC/QD as hospital ship
	17 Oct 1814	22 x 32 carr, 2 x 9s UD; 6 x 32 carr QD; 2 x 9s FC [troopship]
Africaine	11 Aug 1801	6 x 9s, 8 x 32 carr; 4 x 9s, 2 x 32 carr
	12 Aug 1811	14 x 32 carr; 2 x 9s, 2 x 32 carr
Carrère	9 Feb 1802	2 x 9s, 10 x 32 carr; 2 x 9s, 2 x 32 carr

Notes: Tables 60 and 61 are based on the Board of Ordnance summaries of changes in PRO WO 55/1830ff, and probably a better indicator of what was actually supplied to ships than any listing, even the apparently authoritative *Dimensions Books* [DB]. Entries marked [*] have been added from the later Sailing Quality Reports which give the precise armament. The information needs to be used with some sophistication because entries only give detailed breakdowns for departures from the norm of the establishments; ships fitted out with the established armament needed no further comment. The establishments were altered in 1794 and 1799 so, for example, *Lively* did not carry carronades whereas *Alcmene* did, although both were fitted to the establishment then in force.

The date is the Admiralty Order which usually preceded execution by a few days. The armament on each deck is separated by a semi-colon, with the quarterdeck [QD] guns given before those on the forecastle [FC]. If the disposition is unclear in the original source, the total only is given, or separated by a comma if more than one calibre is involved.

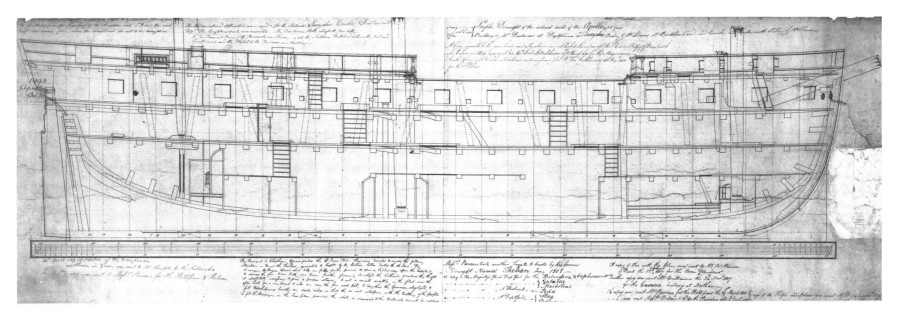

11: Details

Many of the most important features of the arrangements and fittings of frigates have been covered in a previous volume in this series,[134] so this chapter is confined to a few topics of particular relevance to the ships and period under review.

INTERNAL ARRANGEMENTS

The basic layout of the frigate was settled by the time the first 18pdr classes were designed. All had the two magazines which were not yet standard in 12pdr ships,[135] the only variation being their disposition.

Apollo class 36, design profile draught, dated 2 October 1798.

This draught provided the basis for what was the standard 36-gun frigate design of the Napoleonic War, but although a number of topside modifications are mentioned, by this date the internal layout was regarded as virtually fixed in all but minor detail.

Apollo class 36, 1798, design platforms & orlop draught.

Althought the layout of the platforms remained almost unchanged from the first 18pdr frigates, minor improvements in fittings were not ruled out. On this draught, for example, ships following *Apollo* herself were to have the bulkhead between fish room and spirit room deleted, so there was no need for a separate fish room hatch; also, the filling room of the fore magazine was given extended racking for filled cartridges, allowing ships so fitted to keep up sustained rapid firing for longer.

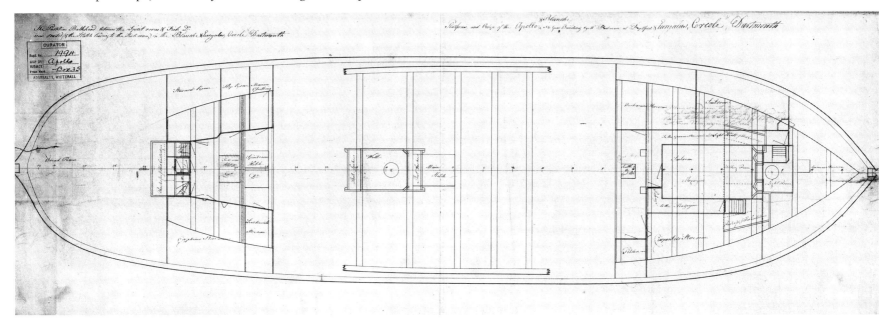

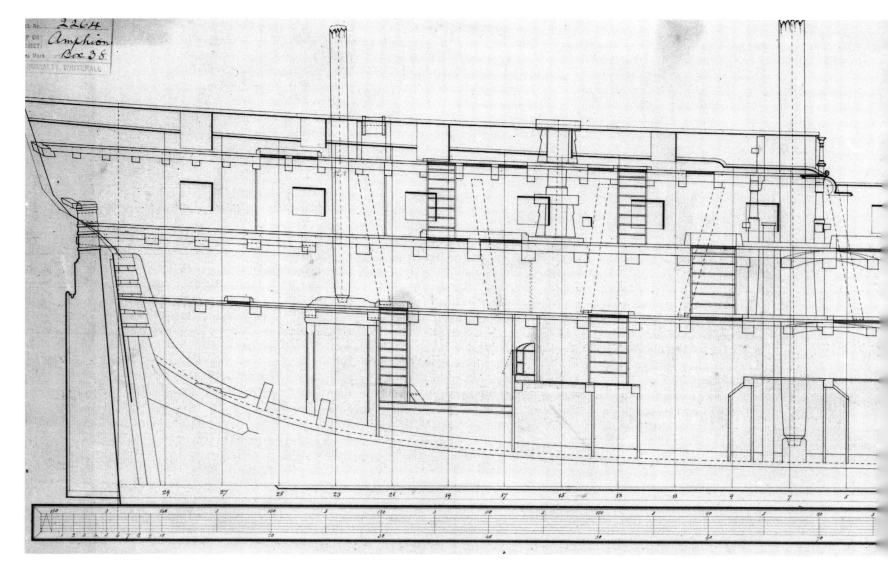

The bigger classes had the main magazine forward, with its filling room and light room under the fore platform; the after magazine was smaller, 'hanging' between the after platform and hold. This arrangement was reversed in the 18pdr 32s, which had a small hanging magazine forward, and the main aft, its palletting being placed lower than the after platform and taking up the full height beneath the lower deck beams. This latter arrangement was presumably the result of the lower depth in hold of the 32s. It is worth pointing out that the *Leda*s, with their French-derived shallow hull, required a hanging main magazine, since it could not be contrived under the fore platform.

For 38s and 36s the fore platform usually contained a central sail room, a small pitch room and large carpenter's store to starboard, with a boatswain's store and second sail room to port, and a gunner's store in the forepeak. The after platform accommodated the captain's and lieutenants' store rooms to starboard, with rooms opposite for the steward, slops, and Marines' uniforms. On the centreline were hatches to the spirits and fish rooms below; access to the hanging magazine was

Amphion class 32, 1796, design profile draught.

Although the later 32s were larger than the earliest 18pdr 36s, the proportions of their hulls meant that it was easier to retain the aft main magazine configuration of earlier ships of that rate. The hanging forward magazine is denoted by dotted lines above and below the fore platform, just aft of the fore mast.

Amphion class 32, 1796, design orlop & platforms draught.

There was little fundamental development in the platform layouts of the 32s between *Pallas* (see Chapter 3) and *Amphion*. The only noteworthy change was a more logical layout of the main (after) magazine, which seems to have allowed more space in the filling room for ready-use cartridges.

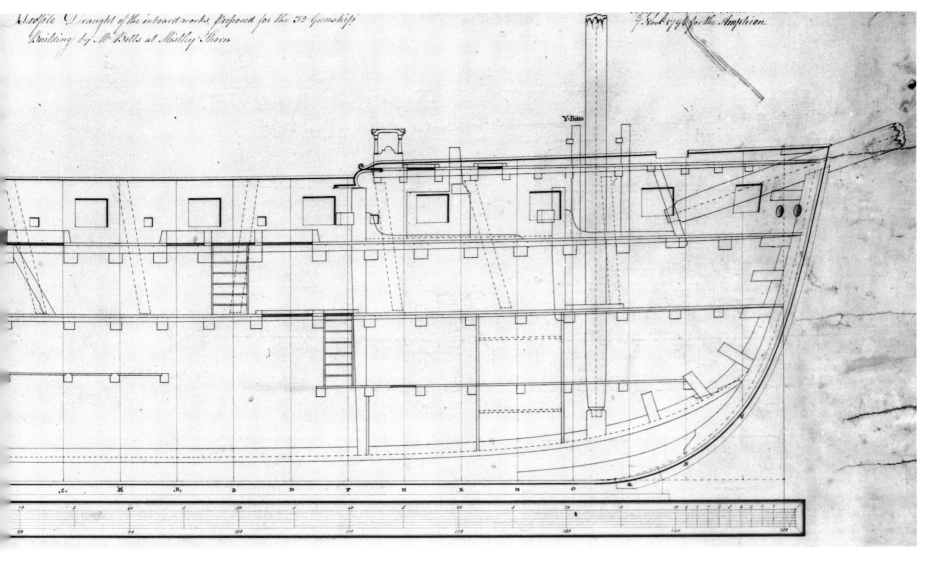

Profile Draught of the inboard works, proposed for the 32 Gunship Building by Mr Betts at Mistley Thorn

9th Feby 1796 for the Amphion.

Y-Bitts

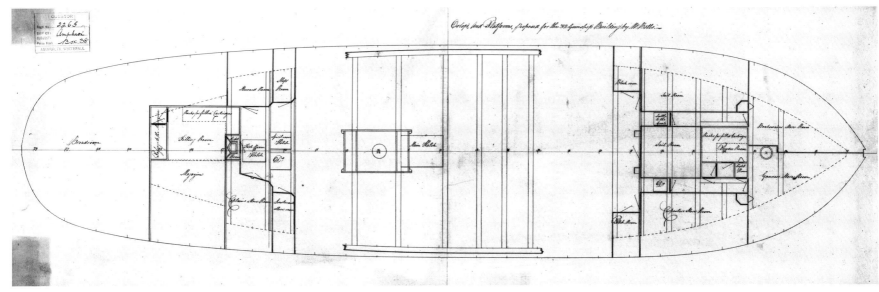

Orlop and Platforms, proposed for the 32 Gunship Building by Mr Betts.

at the rear of the platform, and the space astern of it was the bread room. The 32s had much the same general layout, except for relative size and positioning of some spaces, in order to cope with the reversal of the magazine areas.

On the lower deck, the officers' cabins were arrayed in a single block of six each side of the wardroom space, although the cabins for the captain's clerk, boatswain, gunner and carpenter were beyond the wardroom bulkhead. These last four did not dine in the wardroom, which was confined to the three lieutenants, two Marine officers, master, purser and surgeon – eight in all.

If there were no major changes in the internal layout of frigates in this period, there were a number of small but significant improvements. Perhaps the most important was the introduction of 'air funnels' between the toptimbers to ventilate the lower deck. Following Captain Gore's favourable report on the experiment with *Triton*, in which the extraordinary health of the crew was attributed to the air pipes, an Admiralty Order of 26 April 1797 extended the measure to all new ships 'if it can be done without detriment to their frames'.[136]

It may appear anachronistic that frigates – and large ones at that – were still being designed with oarports in the 1790s. However, it seems certain that they were regarded as useful in certain conditions; they may not have moved the ship very fast (perhaps not at all against a strong tide), but they could give the ship steerage way and a degree of manouevrability in a calm. It is therefore worth recording the sizes of sweep required, as recommended by Deptford Dockyard in 1801: 38-gun ships 60ft; 36-gun ships – 59ft; 32-gun ships – 50ft.[137] These long oars were worked from ports on the upper deck between the gunports.

BOATS

As built, the 38s were established with a 26ft launch, a 30ft pinnace and two 24ft yawls or cutters; 36s seem to have had the same, but the launch may have been the shorter 23ft or 24ft model inherited from the establishment of the 12pdr 36. A four-oared 18ft cutter, which came to be called the jollyboat, was added to all rates by Admiralty Order of 14 June 1781. By the 1790s the pinnace had become a 32ft model and the 24ft boats were invariably cutters for 38s, but it is not clear whether the 36s retained the shorter pinnace or launch. The 18pdr 32s were established as the 12pdr class, with 23/24ft launch, 30ft pinnace, two 24ft cutters and an 18ft jollyboat.

Although quarter davits were not adopted until after 1800, the practice of carrying the jollyboat under fixed davits across the stern was widely employed in the 1790s. This did not meet with Admiralty approval but, despite orders to the contrary, obviously persisted; in October 1798 the Navy Board was reminded that ships were not to be so fitted and the original prohibition was reinforced.[138]

During the 1790s there was a small but significant addition to the firepower of ships in the form of a carronade for the launch. The first establishment, which allowed 12pdrs to vessels of 50-20 guns, was approved on 29 August 1795. They were initially issued with the

continued on page 112

Amelia, 38 guns, ex-French *Proserpine*, as captured sheer & profile draught, dated Plymouth, August 1796.

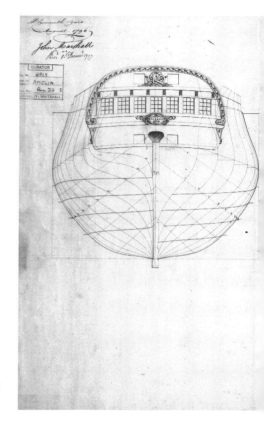

Amelia, 38 guns, ex-French *Proserpine*, as fitted sheer & profile draught, dated Plymouth, 1797.

The draughts of this ship demonstrate very clearly the differences between British and French practice in the fittings and arrangements of big frigates. Comparing the as fitted draught with that taken off immediately after capture, both the head and stern have been reconstructed to reflect British decorative preferences (at this time very austere, with a billet head); taller, solid barricades have replaced the combination of timberheads and low bulwarks, and the barricades have been carried right round the bow; the shed-like *demi-dunette* for the captain on the quarterdeck has been removed and the wheel relocated before the mizzen; also removed were the suction pumps (replaced by one set of chain pumps and one pair of elm tree [suction] pumps), and the forecastle capstan, the funnel of the newly installed galley stove taking its place.

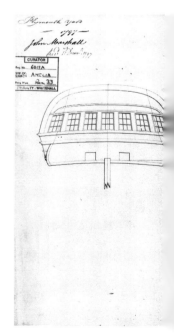

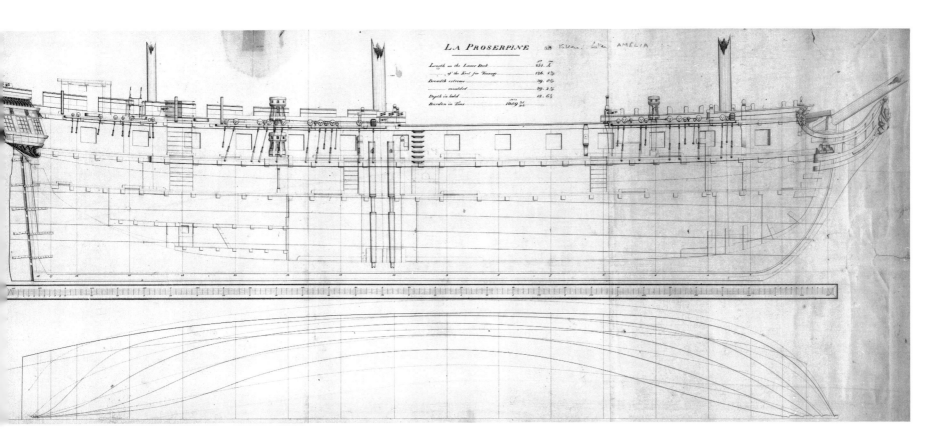

LA PROSERPINE as taken, late AMELIA

Length on the Lower Deck	151. 7
—, of the Keel for Tonnage	126. 1½
Breadth extreme	39. 0¼
moulded	39. 2½
Depth in hold	12. 6½
Burden in Tons	1059 34/94

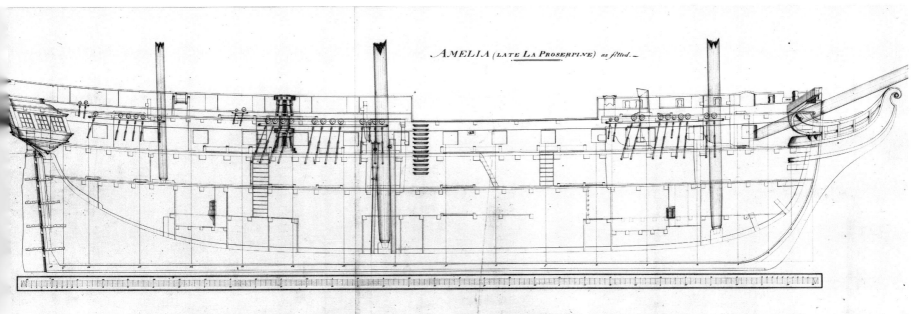

AMELIA (LATE *LA PROSERPINE*) *as fitted.*

Amelia, 38 guns, ex-French *Proserpine*, as captured decks plan, dated Plymouth, August 1796.

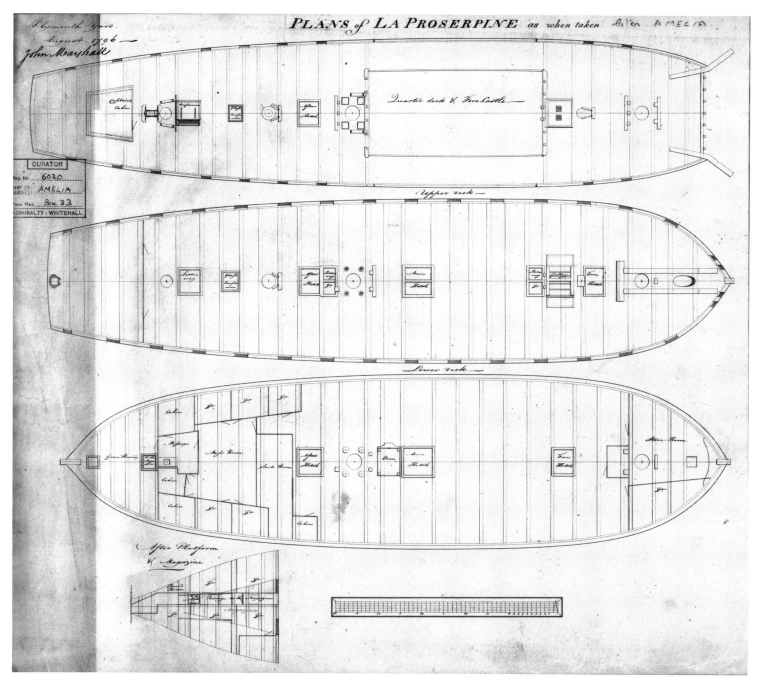

The decks plans reveal further differences between British and French practice. On the forecastle the new bow arrangement is obvious, with the cat tails carried under the deck, out of the way of the chase guns; the quarterdeck is less cluttered, and moving the wheel before the mizzen would have given the helmsman a rather better view (note also the larger diameter capstan). On the upper deck, more and larger hatches and companions were installed, along with a second set of riding bitts. The lower deck arrangement of the French ship included two store rooms forward, and nine cabins aft; six of these were larger than their British equivalent, and what would have been the Royal Navy's wardroom space also

enclosed a large sail room. As fitted, the ship conformed to standard British arrangements. Undoubtedly the greatest differences are to be found in the hold. Whereas the French ship had one small after platform with a magazine below that was very constricted by the sharp section of the after hull, the British added not only an orlop, but a fore platform with a large magazine. The fine lines of the hull and lack of depth in hold made it difficult to adopt standard practice, but the arrangements are as near as could be contrived. On the fore platform the magazine, whose floor is dropped below the level of the platform, takes up most of the space, with boatswain's store and sail room (there is a second on the orlop) to port, and carpenter's store and pitch room to starboard; the gunner's store is in the fore peak. The after platform is more conventional, with a second powder room taking up much of the

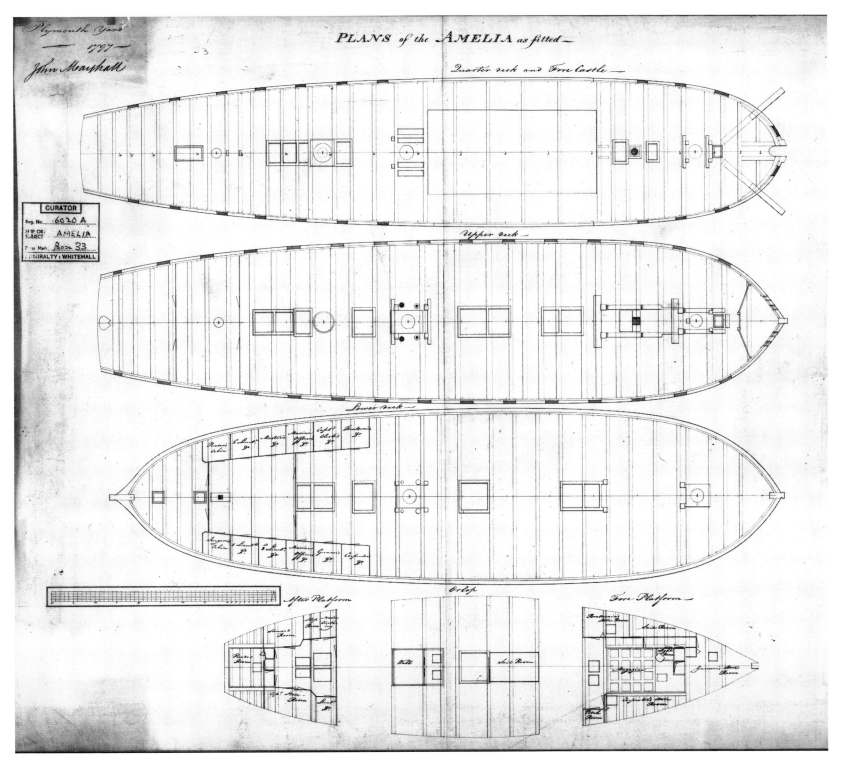

Amelia, 38 guns, ex-French *Proserpine*, as fitted decks plan, dated Plymouth, 1797.

space. These detail differences reveal the British emphasis on sustained firepower (separate and larger magazines), and the self-sufficiency required by long and arduous cruising (manifest in more and bigger store rooms, and better cable-handling arrangements on a separate orlop; even the added security of double riding bitts suggests a navy expecting to ride out the heaviest weather in exposed positions).

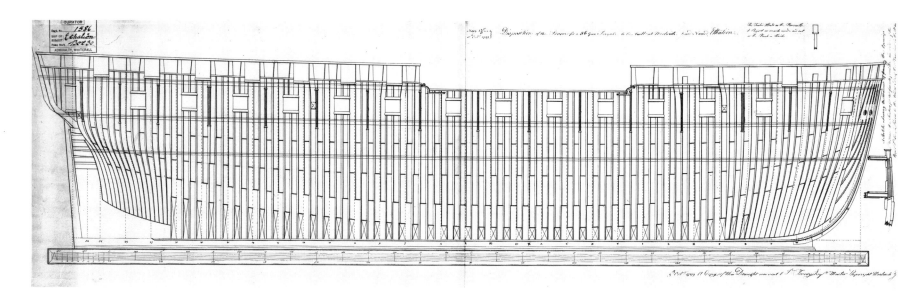

Ethalion, 36 guns, design framing draught, dated 5 October 1799.

The shaded areas between the toptimbers depict the openings for the air pipes, first employed in the *Triton*. The sketch section shows the method of forming them; they run from under the upper deck lodging knees to the underside of the plansheer in the waist or the lodging knees of the forecastle and quarterdeck.

obsolescent 'short' type, until a purpose-designed boat carronade could be cast. The initiative seems to have come from individual commanders, contemplating their employment in support of amphibious operations: much of the detail was worked out by an expedition to the Caribbean, and the standard moveable slides were then fitted 'in the manner of those lately sent to the West Indies'. On 17 August 1796, all ships' launches were ordered to be so fitted, and the boat gun was henceforth to see service in a variety of roles, from cutting-out operations and commando-type raids, to making the launch an armed tender for 'independent' cruising.[139]

BARRICADES

Although solid bulwarks do not appear on draughts before the 1780s, it is clear that in wartime they were widely adopted, if unofficially, then with the tacit acceptance of the authorities.[140] From the introduction of the carronade, this 'berthing up' of the quarterdeck rails became official policy, and, for example, the 1779 order for barricading the *Flora*'s quarters specifies 'to the height of the rough tree rail, which may be done by taking off the planshires and running down intermediate timbers for forming the ports...'.[141] It is possible that the forecastle was also berthed up in some ships, the authoritative Hilhouse model of the *Arethusa* showing this feature (although the dating is uncertain). All solid bulwarks were formally prohibited on 10 August 1786 and the usual peacetime open rails substituted, but as soon as war was again in prospect the Navy Board was inundated with requests from captains for suitable materials. In February 1793 they petitioned the Admiralty for the freedom to allow this modification without express permission from the senior board.[142]

In practice, formal permission may not have been asked because a ship may well have been able to berth up the bulwarks from its own resources. William Dillon describes how his captain ordered the manufacture of such barricades using hawsers twisted around the timberheads and boarded in with light planking.[143] Hawsers would provide good protection against splinters and small arms fire, and may well represent official practice, since the boards alone would offer scant defence. Whatever their form, it is clear that many frigates had berthed up forecastles almost from the beginning of the war, and forecastle barricades finally appear on design draughts from 1798.[144]

APPEARANCE

The most significant development of the period was the extreme decorative austerity of the 1790s. The order of May 1796 to 'explode carved works altogether'[145] is often quoted, but as far as frigates are concerned the new puritanism was already in evidence. The design sheer draught of the *Alcmene* class, dated March 1793, shows a billet head; and, considering that they were a war emergency measure, it is not surprising that the fir-built ships of the 1795 programme also reveal this economy. Of the oak ships, *Hydra* and *Boadicea* show it (although it looks like an alteration to the draught), but not *Sirius* or *Naiad*. Curiously, there is no trace of it on the draughts of ships designed nearest to the prohibition (*Active*, *Amazon* and *Leda*), although the fir-built *Triton* carries one.

It seems that the order was intended to extend the minimalist decoration already practised on smaller ships to the line of battle. This met considerable resistance from Navy Board and dockyards, which regarded the restrictions an affront to the navy and the nation. The attitude is best summed up by the Navy Board's response to a later proposal for straight headrails: 'for the sake of uniformity and the credit of HM Ships, which have hitherto been considered patterns to every nation, we cannot recommend it.'[146] The navy's 'credit' or prestige was too

Pomone, 38 guns, 1805, contemporary model.

This rather crude 1/60 scale model is said to represent the second *Leda* class 38. Its main interest lies in the deck detail, including a full outfit of boats. If this model depicts the ship as completed in 1805, it is worth noting that there are no quarter davits as yet, but a small cutter is carried under the fixed stern davits.

important to be sacrificed for a small saving and by September 1797 a revised head and stern for 74s was regarded as standard;[147] at about the same time permission, even if only tacit, must have been given for a similar bust-type figure to be reinstated on frigates. Nevertheless, in general the order of 1796 abolished for ever the elaborate carved work of trailboard, quarters and stern, which combined with less colourful paint schemes, square-hanced built-up barricades, and a flatter sheer line to point the frigate towards the cold, classical appearance of the nineteenth century.

Flora, 36 guns, as fitted sheer & profile draught, dated Deptford, 14 April 1780.

As the first 18pdr ship to complete, and the first to carry carronades from the outset, *Flora* obviously needed particular attention in fitting out. This unusually detailed draught was probably intended as the blueprint for fitting all the first generation 18pdr frigates, and there is a separate drawing of the quarterdeck barricades in the Deptford Dockyard records. Not only does the draught show the external relationship between solid bulwarks, hammock netting cranes and swivel stocks, but also depicts the various kevels, cleats and other belaying points inside them.

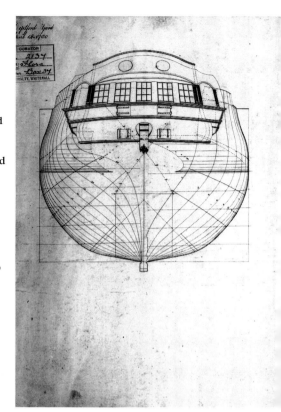

Arethusa 38 guns, 1781, contemporary model.

This is one of a quartet of very fine models associated with the Hilhouse shipbuilding company of Bristol. This model is highly detailed, including internal fittings revealed by the unplanked starboard side, the only question about its authenticity being the exact point in the ship's long career depicted by the model. The solid forecastle barricade has been used to argue for a date about 1800, but it is known that these were employed earlier; however, the stern davits suggest the 1790s, as do the flush gangways. In other respects the model is very carefully constructed so the fact that the model carries only six carronades (four on the quarterdeck) must be treated seriously; it is known that the ship carried six 18pdrs in this disposition in 1782, whereas she mounted a full battery of 32pdrs from 1793. It would be convenient if the model's carronades were 18pdrs, but as far as one can judge at 1/48 scale they appear to be of the later model (with nozzle), although there is no attempt to model a screw elevating gear. It is possible that the model was built in the early 1790s (like the *Melampus* reproduced earlier), perhaps before the new carronade armament was widely known, or possibly intentionally replicating the armament that would have been most familiar to the builders – assuming they commissioned the construction of the model. *(Bristol Museum and Art Gallery)*

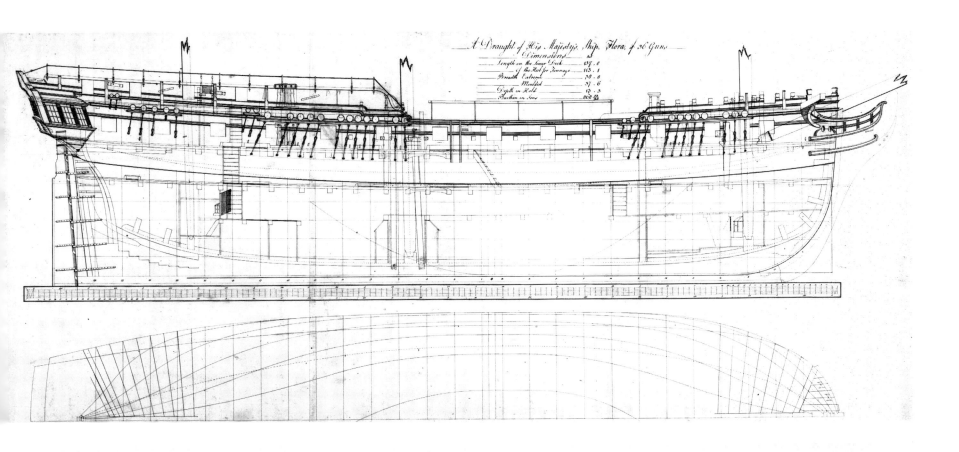

A Draught of His Majesty's Ship Flora of 36 Guns.

Alcmene class 32, design sheer draught, dated 22 February 1793.

This is the earliest frigate draught to show the austerity billet head and clearly anticipates the famous order of May 1796 to 'explode carved works altogether'. Individually modelled figures were reintroduced to frigates later, but only in in the attenuated form of a bust, rather than a full-length carving.

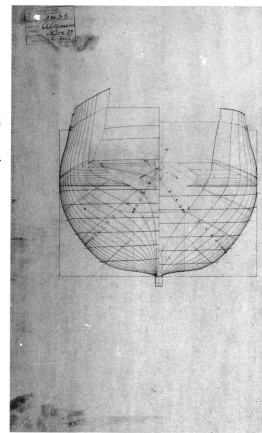

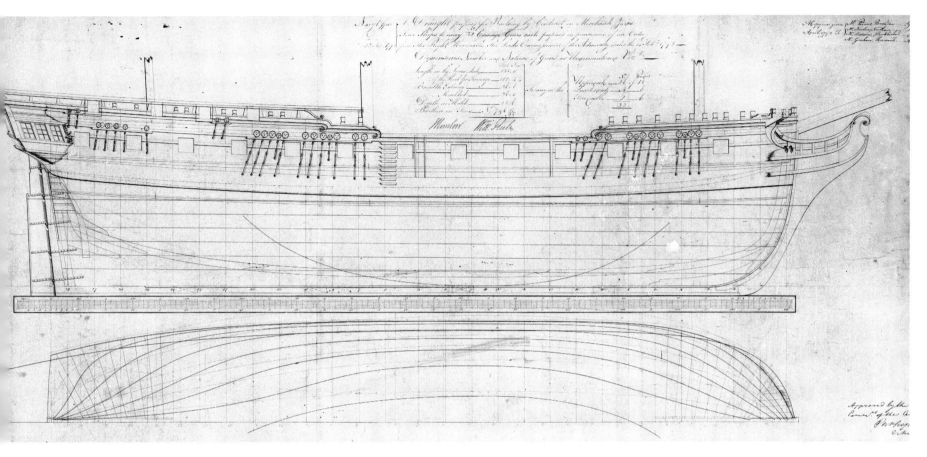

Notes

[1] See the author's chapter 'The Frigate' in *The Line of Battle* (Conway's History of the Ship series) for an outline history of early cruising ship development in general and these ships in particular.

[2] For example, a 1719 Establishment 40-gun ship carried 0.3 pounds of broadside firepower per ton, compared with only 0.16 per ton for a 20-gun Sixth Rate.

[3] Defined as a vessel with a complete but unarmed lower deck, positioned around the load waterline; there were isolated examples earlier but the French *Medée* of 1744 is usually credited with popularising the type.

[4] In modern times the *Graf Spee* might be cited as a similar super-raider; at fleet level the individual superiority of a *Bismarck* or *Yamato* was helpless when faced with greater numbers.

[5] Information from Jean Boudriot's monograph *La Vénus* (Paris 1979), p2; and *La Frégate* (Paris 1993), pp118-121, which reproduces a drawing of the 1769 design.

[6] Minuted on the back of the Navy Board's reply of 20 June 1757 (NMM ADM/B/156).

[7] Jean Boudriot, *La Vénus*, p3.

[8] Jean Boudriot, *La Frègate*, pp97.

[9] He was, for example, a founder member of the Society for the Improvement of Naval Architecture.

[10] NMM ADM/B/197.

[11] NRS *Barham* II, pp178-9 letter to Howe (then at the Admiralty), 16 Nov 1784 repeating his deposition to the King some three years previously.

[12] A second was under discussion towards the end of the war but the contract was never concluded. PRO Adm 2/257, 14 Nov 1782.

[13] See the author's *The First Frigates* (London 1992), pp45-6.

[14] In the peace years after 1763 Kempenfelt made regular visits to France to study the theory and practice of shipbuilding, and became an advocate of French-style technical training. *Naval Chronicle* VII (1802), p362

[15] NRS *Barham* I, pp335-6, letter of 11 Nov 1780.

[16] *Perseverance* and *Inconstant*, built by large Thames yards seem to have spent less time on the stocks, but considering time from contract the generalisation holds good. Even 32s were rarely built any faster.

[17] Anecdotal evidence reinforces the Sailing Quality reports. See, for example, NRS *Miscellany* I, p270: William Cathcart expressed himself pleased to leave the *Romulus* for 'a fine new ship that sails decently'.

[18] Earl St Vincent regarded them as all a frigate should be and ordered a repeat class in 1801; see Vol II of this study. They were also lengthened to form the the *Phoebe* class of 1794.

[19] PRO Adm 106/2209, 9 Nov 1781 and 23 Mar 1782.

[20] PRO Adm 2/257, Admiralty Order 11 Jan 1783.

[21] She was probably the best British-built frigate of the day and regarded as a plum command. Byam Martin records HRH Prince William's pique at not getting the

ship in 1788: NRS *Byam Martin* I, p126.

22 Sailing Quality report, PRO Adm 95/36, 27 Nov 1788.

23 Based on the logs, PRO Adm 51/360 and NMM/L/F/149, adjusted for woundings that proved fatal. *Flora*'s broadside (with 8 x 18pdr carr onades) was 351lbs to *Nymphe*'s 174, but she later landed 2 carronades.

24 A good example is Kempenfelt's correspondence with Middleton (NRS *Barham* I, pp288-370), which is replete with instances of what he felt was an eminently superior attitude to naval improvements in France.

25 No draught survives and certainly the correspondence indicates that one was never sent to the Admiralty for approval.

26 PRO Adm 106/ 2209, 14 Jan, 18 Mar and 27 Mar 1782.

27 NRS *Barham* II, p184.

28 NMM ADM/BP/10, 16 Jul 1790. The measure was intended to free the Dockyards to deal with fitting out line of battle ships.

29 NRS *Barham* II, pp198ff.

30 PRO Adm 2/267, 12 Dec 1790: the complete programme was a 50 and sloop (Deptford), a Second Rate (Woolwich), Second Rate, 32 and sloop (Chatham), a 50 and 32 (Portsmouth) and a First Rate and 32 (Plymouth).

31 Sixteen were still in service: see *Naval Chronicle* I (1799), p541 for list at March 1793 (one name is different but it otherwise agrees with the ships listed by Jean Boudriot in *La Vénus*, pp20-23).

32 William James, *The Naval History of Great Britain* (1837 edition), Vol I, p56.

33 Sailing Quality report on *Diana*, PRO Adm 95/46, 27 Feb 1812.

34 Published in 1791 (see p13). Warren went on to command a very successful Channel cruiser squadron which at various times included a number of these 'short' 18pdr frigates; rarely did opponents escape.

35 Brian Lavery, *The Ship of the Line*, Vol I, p125.

36 NRS *Barham* II, p367: memorandum of 1793 possibly intended for Lord Chatham to whom he was an unofficial adviser, even before joining the Admiralty.

37 The 10,000 men of 'the grand old Duke of York', familiar from the satirical song.

38 In 1793 there were reported to be about ten 74s and thirty-nine smaller two-deckers; there were few frigates with more than 12pdrs and most ships were in a poor state. James Vol I, pp54-55.

39 PRO Adm 8/73.

40 NRS *Barham* II, p401; letter from Captain Philip Patton.

41 See the author's *The First Frigates*, pp16-19.

42 PRO Adm 95/85 contains scantlings lists for Dockyard-built ships, 1794-1807.

43 A modern study calculated that the North Sea experiences winds of Force 5 and above (Sea State 4 and upwards) for 64 per cent of the year.

44 It took some time for the virtues of fir ships to be appreciated: Byam Martin complained of the *Tamer*'s 'uncertain qualities' on first acquaintance but came to love his 'noble fast-sailing ship'. NRS *Byam Martin* I, 271; III, 289

45 PRO Adm 2/306: *Clyde* 'whose qualities have been much approved', 19 Oct 1804.

46 This is probably why the Progress Books do not give Ordering dates for ships from about 1780 onwards and again from the late 1790s.

47 PRO Adm 2/274 and Adm 106/2219; letters of 23 and 26 January 1795 in the latter give a complete list of builders and the classes they proposed to contract for.

48 See, for example, Brian Lavery *The Ship of the Line*, Vol I, pp121- 125.

49 St Vincent's Admiralty ordered the *Forte* to the lines of the *Révolutionnare* in 1801, the only example of an entirely new design, although *Courageux*-derived battleships continued to be built.

50 See R Morriss, *The Royal Dockyards during the Revolutionary and Napoleonic Wars* (Leicester 1983), p46 on Parliament's 'very general wish and expectation... that something should be done'.

51 The preamble setting out the terms of reference for Samuel Bentham's new office of Inspector-General of Naval Works, undated but around Mar 1796. PRO Adm 1/3525.

52 NRS *Markham*, pp312-3. '[French attention to mathematical and mechanical sciences] will give them an incalculable advantage in the field, and in time may check our superiority by sea if we neglect a similar culture.'

53 'The man who first thought of appointing carpenters to direct the construction of the navy has a grievous sin to answer for', Captain Thomas Hamilton to Admiral Markham, 1806: *ibid*, pp335-6.

54 *Ibid*, p348.

55 Smith to Spencer, 21 Jul 1795; the author is indebted to Richard Saxby for this reference, taken from research for his forthcoming NRS volume on the blockade of Brest.

56 Very few French 18pdr frigates mounted only twenty-six upper deck guns (which were rated 38s in the French navy), but some '40s' seem to have qualified by virtue of a bow chase port suitable for arming.

57 Comparing figures given in PRO Adm 95/68-70. Weight of provisions was an additional variable but the discrepancies between the totals of iron shingle and water is too great for it to challenge the generalisation.

58 PRO Adm 106/2223, 16 Feb 1798.

59 NRS *Markham*, p3; letter of 16 Apr 1802.

60 For a description of the famous *Dart* and *Arrow* and the schooners, see John Fincham, *A History of Marine Architecture*, pp130-132

61 The ship was completed with 12pdrs and is covered in the author's previous book, *The First Frigates*. However, she was designed for 18pdrs which justifies including new information here.

62 Vol II (1799), pviii. The author is indebted to Derek Andrews for this reference, which made the other pieces of the puzzle fall into place.

63 See David Cordingly, *Nicholas Pocock* (London 1986), p80; he attributes the design to the wrong Gambier, the uncle rather than to the nephew.

64 St Vincent, a successful fighting admiral but failed administrator, dismissed one admiral as 'like Lord Barham and Admiral Gambier, a compound of paper and packthread.' NRS *Markham*, p50.

65 *Ibid*, p347. Captain Thomas Hamilton about a joint scheme of Gambier's with Henry Peake, Master Shipwright at Deptford and later a Surveyor.

66 By the *Naval Chronicle*; quoted in *Memorials, Personal and Historical of Admiral Lord Gambier*, edited by Lady Chatterton (London 1861), Vol I, pp345-6.

67 *Ibid*, p345, apparently quoting a letter in Gambier's papers from the builders, Barnard & Co.

68 Bentham also later tried to get some of these features incorporated in to the *Circe* class of fir 32s, which he regarded as expendable enough to justify experimentation. NMM ADM/Y/1, 15 Aug 1804.

69 NMM ADM/A/2896, 21 Jul 1797.

70 William Cathcart, who served in the ship in 1800-1801, said 'She is allowed to be one of the fastest ships in the navy.' NRS *Miscellany* II, p288.

71 PRO Adm 2/281, 26 Apr 1797; the specifications in Adm 95/85 from 1798 include this feature.

72 The obvious parallel is the Second World War 'Castle' class corvette. The Admiralty wanted 'River' class frigates, but the 'Castles' were designed to use yards that were to small for 'Rivers'.

73 PRO Adm 2/614, letter from the Secretary 11 Jun 1796.

74 Henslow later told St Vincent that the Surveyors had not favoured the the increase in sizes but had resisted Admiralty pressure as far as possible. NRS *Miscellany* II, pp330, 6 Nov 1800.

75 PRO Adm 2/289, 7 Sep 1799.

76 Gambier was related to Melville and was invited to rejoin the Board, an offer he promptly accepted.

77 PRO Adm 1/2512, 14 Oct 1804.

78 Captain's comments in Sailing Quality report, 12 Sep 1815; PRO Adm 95/ 48.

79 NRS *Barham* III, pp18-20.

80 In fact no new French 18pdr ships were laid down after 1814, but some remained on the slips for many years, the last being launched in 1823.

81 Brian Lavery, *The Ship of the Line*, Vol I, p123.

82 NRS *Spencer* III, p9, 18 Jun 1799. It is worth noting that the requirements of a frigate were the same whether or not the battlefleet was involved in close blockade, since they usually held the inshore stations.

83 Lord Spencer was very reluctant to allow any on Foreign Service: see his Memo on Admiral Christian's request for heavy frigates for the West Indies, 24 Aug 1795, in NRS *Spencer* I, pp145-46.

84 *Letter from Gabriel Snodgrass, Esq to Rt Hon Henry Dundas... on the Mode of Improving the Navy of Great Britain* (London 1797), p10.

85 NRS *Byam Martin* I, p318.

86 The author is indebted to Richard Saxby for this reference.

87 It is possible to get some impression of performance from the similar lists in PRO Adm 180/24 and NMM RUSI/NM/74, which give speeds; but other aspects are hidden behind the compiler's personal hieroglyphics.

88 PRO Adm 95/39, Sailing Quality report, 9 Apr 1802.

89 NMM MID/8/1, undated: lists Gravesend, Ipswich, Wivenhoe, Bristol, Burseldon, Mistleythorn, Sandwich, Dover and Sandgate (some of these had built warships, but not in recent memory).

90 See the author's *The First Frigates*, p42.

91 The fastening of some of the 74s of the late 1790s with 'devil bolts' (which had a visible head but no shank) was a *cause celèbre* and used by St Vincent's Admiralty as a reason for not employing contract building.

92 Of the 28-gun ships of 1782, only the *Laurel* was cancelled but some builders in the Dover area had to combine to complete their ships.

93 PRO Adm 2/310, 20 Oct 1806.

94 *Syren* and *Doris* were cancelled in June 1806 after the failure of the Appledore builder Record. Tanner's bankruptcy left *Dartmouth* and *Creole* unfinished, causing the Navy Board much trouble to get them completed.

95 Brindley was so convinced that it was safe that he offered to build the frigate at his own risk or to have it insured by Lloyds; the Navy Board was unmoved. PRO Adm 106/1457, 22 & 31 Jul 1805.

96 PRO Adm 106/2220, 26 Jun 1795.

97 For example, Brindley successfully requested a repeat *Pomone* in 1803, and Ross a second *Resistance* in 1805.

98 This may account for the *Dimensions Book* endorsement 'Of old oak', but it is unlikely that it was used throughout. Nevertheless, the author's statement in *The First Frigates*, p57, needs modification.

99 PRO Adm 2/317, 10 Apr 1809.

100 Ironically, France had been trying to impose greater standardisation, worked out by the Chevalier de Borda, Inspector of Naval Construction from 1784 and Jacques-Noel Sané, his most gifted designer.

101 See his correspondence with Sir Sidney Smith on the subject, referred to in Footnote 86.

102 See Chapter 5, Footnote 66.

103 There are a number of letters between St Vincent and Markham on this theme, particularly leading up to Henslow's retirement in 1806.

104 At this period it was clearly a gunport because the Admiralty specified that the extra port for the *Amphion* was not to have one of the broadside guns regularly allocated to it, PRO Adm 2/614, 11 Jun 1796.

105 Jean Boudriot, *La Frégate*, p113.

106 PRO Adm 106/2218, 29 Jan 1794.

107 'Remarks on the Form and Properties of Ships', *Naval Chronicle* IX (1803), pp33ff.

108 NMM ADM/Y/2, 20 Jun 1805: a note in the file says there are so many 'of character' that only one each of the most approved can be sent.

109 Peake, who just become Junior Surveyor, said as much in a letter of 9 Sep 1806: NMM ADM/Y/5.

110 Spencer to Smith, 11 Jul 1795. Reference from Richard Saxby.

111 Captain's report on the *Pique*, 22 Jan 1812, PRO Adm 95/46.

112 Asked by the Commission of Naval Enquiry about the wisdom of so many varieties of classes, Sir William Rule replied that they at least retained standard spar dimensions and stores. *Naval Chronicle* X (1803), p43

113 Dimensions for the yard and its sail for various classes are dated 27 Apr 1797, although there is not much evidence for its employment until after the war. NMM CHA/K/1, 27 Apr 1797.

114 *Naiad* is the only known exception, but she was a one-off and may be regarded as non-standard; the only other known request is from the captain of the *Stag*, for taller lower masts, and that was turned down.

115 NRS *Spencer* I, p254: letter from Sir John Borlase Warren, 7 Aug 1796.

116 In a full gale while pursuing the privateer *Bordelaise*, 15 Oct 1799. *Naval Chronicle* II (1799), p535.

117 See the author's *The First Frigates*, p81.

118 In trials carried out in August 1790 the 18pdr showed up badly against 12s, 24s and 32s at point blank range although better than the 12 at 2 degrees elevation; this seems to have been an 8ft gun. PRO Adm 1/4014.

119 PRO Adm 106/2219, 22 Nov 1794.

120 PRO Adm 106/2087, 19 Feb 1795.

121 PRO WO 55/1831 & 1832.

122 PRO Adm 2/251, AOs 22 & 25 Apr 1780.

123 NMM ADM/L/F/148-9; PRO Adm 51/360.

124 PRO Adm 2/255, 21 January 1782.

[124] PRO Adm 2/255, 21 January 1782.

[125] NRS *Dillon*, Vol I, pp66 & 72. However, this was in January 1793 before the actual outbreak of war.

[126] PRO Adm 1/4014, 30 Jul 1793.

[127] For example, *Unicorn*'s captain: PRO Adm 106/2219, 25 Aug 1794.

[128] PRO Adm 1/4014, 25 Aug 1795. Frigates concerned (and carronades needed) were: Jason (6), *Minerva, Caroline, Phoebe, Doris, Emerald, Hebe, Undaunted, Amethyst, Topaze* and *Imperieuse* (all needing 8).

[129] PRO Adm 106/2225, 31 May 1795. Ships concerned were:*Galatea* (10 x 24s); *Apollo, Jason, Aigle, Hussar, Active, Leda, Boadicea* (14 x 32s); French prizes *Modeste, Gloire* (12 x 32s), *Immortalité, Decade* (14 x 32s).

[130] PRO Adm 2/306, Admiralty Order of 17 Dec 1804 concerning frigates refitting.

[131] PRO Adm 1/4016 & 4017.

[132] PRO Adm 106/3474, 2 Oct 1804 Henslow to Master Shipwright at Deptford, concerning the *Melampus* which should have had an all-carronade armament on the quarterdeck but with two different types of mounting.

[133] Agreed by AO 3 Feb 1794, PRO Adm 106/2217.

[134] See the author's *The First Frigates*, (London 1992).

[135] A drawing in PRO Adm 106/3472, dated 10 May 1781, shows the arrangements for the new forward powder room in 28s and 32s.

[136] PRO Adm 2/281.

[137] PRO Adm 106/3325, 14 Jan 1801.

[138] PRO Adm 106/2088, 27 Oct 1798.

[139] PRO Adm 106/2088, 11 Aug 1795 (issue of short type); 25 Aug 1796 (moveable slides).

[140] See the present writer's *The First Frigates*, p71

[141] PRO Adm 95/96, 3 Oct 1779. *Flora* was obviously the ship on which these arrangements were worked out, hence the very detailed draught and drawing in the Deptford Dockyard records.

[142] There are numerous captains' requests in PRO Adm 106/2086; the Navy Board's petition to the Admiralty is in PRO Adm 106/2217.

[143] NRS *Dillon*, exact ref needed.

[144] The *Apollo* draught was approved in Sep 1798 except that the 'rails of the forecastle should be filled up in the same manner as the quarterdeck.' PRO Adm 2/286. The *Lively* was similarly modified in Dec 1799.

[145] PRO Adm 106/2088, 15 May 1796. It goes on to except 'mouldings about the scroll or billet head, the stern and quarters'.

[146] PRO Adm 106/2237, 22 Mar 1804, responding to a suggestion from commissioner Coffin. On investigation it proved notably cheaper, and was eventually adopted, a step towards the solid headrails of later decades.

[147] PRO Adm 106/2223, 21 Sep 1797.

Sources

This book is based largely on primary sources, notably the huge Admiralty Collection of draughts, and official correspondence between the principal bodies of the naval administration (Admiralty, Navy Board and the Royal Dockyards). Most of the draughts are now kept at the National Maritime Museum, Greenwich, as are some of the documents; most of the latter are to be found at the Public Record Office, Kew. Because the period covered by this book has been the subject of much study, there are also selected secondary sources that have proved useful, and these are listed after the documents.

DRAUGHTS

The following is a list of plans consulted but not quite a complete list of everything available. As pointed out in *The First Frigates*, many of the draughts relate to more than one ship, or even the whole class, which has led to some variation in the cataloguing of the collection over the years. Certainly, the attribution in the original Admiralty Librarian's stamp is not infallible, and in the following list an attempt has been made to clarify the position. For British-built ships the draughts are usually design plans unless marked 'as built'.

The following abbreviations indicate the types of draught: S = sheer (lines and external appearance); P = profile (internal elevation); S&P = combined sheer and profile (on the original the internal works are conventionally represented in red ink, the exterior in black); Ds = plan of decks; QD&FC = quarterdeck and forecastle; UD = upper deck; LD = lower deck; Pl = platforms (and usually orlop); F = frame. Specifications, where noted, are from Adm 168, currently on loan from the PRO to the NMM.

Admiralty Collection, National Maritime Museum

38-GUN SHIPS

Minerva class
Class	LD, UD, QD&FC, specification
Minerva	S&P
Phaeton	S&P
Thetis	S, P, Pl, LD, UD, QD&FC, F

Latona class
Latona	S, P, Pl, LD, UD, QD&FC, F

Beaulieu
Beaulieu	S, P, Pl, LD, UD, QD&FC

Artois class
Class	S, P, Pl, LD, UD, QD&FC, F (also inboard and outboard planking expansions attributed to this class)
Fir ships	S
Jason	S
Ethalion	S, P, Pl, LD, UD, QD&FC, F

Naiad
Naiad	S, P, F

Boadicea
Boadicea	S, P, Pl, LD, UD, QD&FC, F

Hydra
Hydra	S, P, Pl, LD, UD, QD&FC, F

Active
Active	S, P, Pl, LD, UD, QD&FC,

Amazon class
Class	S, P, Pl, LD, UD, QD&FC, F

Leda class
Class	S, P, Pl, LD, UD, QD&FC, F (many later plans – see Vol II)

Lively class
Class	S, P, Pl, LD, UD, QD&FC, F, specification (many later plans – see Vol II)
Lively	As built: 1/16in = 1ft scale pictorial S&P

36-GUN SHIPS

Flora class
Class and	S, P, Pl, LD, UD, QD&FC, F, stern (for *Thalia* *Crescent*)
Flora	As built: S&P, LD, UD, QD&FC, F
Crescent	As built: S&P
Romulus	S

Perseverance class
Class	S, P, Pl, LD, UD, QD&FC, specification
Phoenix	S&P

Melampus
Melampus	S, Pl, LD, UD, QD&FC, specification

Phoebe class
Class	
(*Caroline*)	S, P, Pl, LD, UD, QD&FC, F
(*Dryad*)	specification
Doris	S
Dryad	S

Amazon class
Class	S, P, Pl, LD, UD, QD&FC, F
Fir ships	S

Sirius
Sirius	S, P, Pl, LD, UD, QD&FC, F

Penelope class
Class	No plans

Apollo class
Apollo/Blanche	S, P, Pl, LD, UD, QD&FC, F
Euryalus	S; midship section (1815)

Aigle class
Class	S, P, Pl, LD, UD, QD&FC, F, specification

Ethalion
Ethalion	S, P, Pl, LD, UD, QD&FC, F

32-GUN SHIPS

Pallas class

Class	S, P, Pl, LD, UD, QD&FC, F, stern
Alcmene class	
Class	S, P, Pl, LD, UD, QD&FC, F, stern
Amphion class	
Amphion	S, P, Pl, LD, UD, QD&FC, F, specification
Aeolus/Medusa	S, P, Pl, LD, UD, QD&FC, F
Narcissus class	
Class	S, P, Pl, LD, UD, QD&FC, F, specification

FRENCH PRIZES (by date of capture)

Captured 1778-83

Artois	As captured: S&P
Hebe	As fitted: S&P, Ds
Aigle	As refitted 1790: S&P, internal and external
planking	
	expansions

Captured 1793-1801

Amethyst [ex-Perle]	S&P, Pl, LD, UD, QD&FC
Aréthuse 1795:	S&P, Pl, LD, UD, QD&FC
Impérieuse	As fitted: S&P, LD, UD, QD&FC
Modeste	S&P
San Fiorenzo	As fitted: S&P, UD, QD&FC [ex-Minerve]
Sybille	As captured: S&P, LD, UD, QD&FC; 1815
repairs:	
	P
Melpomène	As fitted: S&P, LD, UD, QD&FC
Révolutionnaire	As captured: S&P, LD, UD, QD&FC; 1812
repairs:	
	P; 1818 repairs: Pl
Minerve	S&P, Pl, LD, UD, QD&FC
Virginie	As captured: S&P, Ds; as fitted: P, Ds
Amelia	As captured: S&P, P, Ds; as fitted: P, Ds
[ex-Proserpine]	
Uranie [ex-Tartu]	As captured: S&P, Ds; as fitted: P, Ds
Fisgard	As captured: S&P; as fitted: S&P
[ex-Réistance]	
Seine	S&P, Pl, LD, UD, QD&FC
Loire	As captured: S&P, Ds; as fitted: Ds
Immortalité	As fitted: S&P, Ds (¹/₈th scale)
Princess	As fitted: S&P, Pl, LD, UD, QD&FC
Charlotte [ex-Junon]	
Pique [ex-Pallas]	As fitted: S&P, Ds, alterations, bow detail (chain cable)
Desirée	As fitted: S&P, LD, UD, QD&FC
Niobe	1803: stern; 1810: S&P, Ds, Pl; 1814 as troopship:
[ex-Diane]	P, LD, UD, QD&FC

Africaine	1802 (as captured?): S&P, Pl, LD, UD, QD&FC

DUTCH PRIZES

Captured 1793-1801

Tholin	No plans
Saldanha	No plans

DOCUMENTS

As pointed out in the previous volume in this series, *The First Frigates*, little of the vast collection of surviving official correspondence relates to design matters or procurement policy. Serious students are referred to the remarks on individual series of documents in the earlier volume, most of which apply to this study as well. Notes below are confined to documents of particular relevance to this volume.

A. Public Records Office

Adm 1/. Admiralty In Letters

Adm 2/. Admiralty Out Letters

Adm 8/. Station Lists

Adm 12/. Admiralty Secretary In Letters – Digests and indexes

Adm 51/. Captains' Logs

Adm 95/. Controller's Office Miscellanea

Adm 106/. Navy Board Letters Includes Deptford Dockyard correspondence, 106/3319ff.

Adm 168/. Contracts and Specifications. On loan to the National Maritime Museum.

Adm 180/. Progress and Dimensions Books

WO 55/. [War Office] Board of Ordnance Miscellanea. Includes a very valuable register of orders relating to armament changes to warships that seems more reliable than the *Dimensions Books* for guns actually shipped.

B. National Maritime Museum

ADM/A/. Admiralty Out Letters to Navy Board

ADM/B/ and ADM/BP/. Admiralty In Letters from Navy Board

ADM/L/F/. Lieutenants' Logs

ADM/Y/. Admiralty In Letters from Navy Board Respecting the Fitting of Ships, 1804-1810

CHA/K/. Chatham Dockyard Records: Index and Abstract of Navy Board Orders

MID/. Papers of Sir Charles Middleton

POR/A/. Portsmouth Dockyard Records: Officers' Warrants from Navy Board

POR/D/. Portsmouth Dockyard Records: Officers' Reports

SPB/15. Letters and Naval Memoranda of Captain Edward Rotherham, 1787-1830.

RUSI/NM/. Navy Lists

BOOKS AND ARTICLES

(Navy Records Society volumes are cited in the notes as NRS and a shortened version of the title)

JEAN BOUDRIOT, *La Vénus* (Paris 1979).

—, *La Frégate* (Paris 1992).

LADY CHATTERTON (ed), *Memorials, Personal and Historical of Admiral Lord Gambier*, 2 vols (London 1861).

JULIAN S CORBETT (ed), *Private Papers of George, second Earl Spencer*, Vols I & II, Navy Records Society (London 1913-14).

JOHN FINCHAM, *A History of Marine Architecture* (London 1851).

ROBERT GARDINER, 'The Frigate', in ROBERT GARDINER (ed), *The Line of Battle* (London 1992).

—, *The First Frigates* (London 1992).

SIR RICHARD VESEY HAMILTON (ed), *Letters and Papers of Sir Thomas Byam Martin*, Navy Record Society, 3 vols (London 1898-1903).

WILLIAM JAMES, *The Naval History of Great Britain*, 6 vols (revised ed, London 1837).

SIR JOHN KNOX LAUGHTON (ed), *The Naval Miscellany*, Vol I, Navy Records Society (London 1901).

—, *Letters and Papers of Charles, Lord Barham*, Navy Records Society, 3 vols (London 1907-11).

—, *The Naval Miscellany*, Vol II, Navy Records Society (London 1912).

BRIAN LAVERY, *The Ship of the Line*, 2 vols (London 1983-84).

—, *The Arming and Fitting of English Ships of War*, 1600-1815 (London 1987).

MICHAEL A LEWIS (ed), *Sir William Dillon's Professional Adventures, 1790-1839*, 2 vols, Navy Record Society (London 1952 & 1956).

SIR CLEMENTS MARKHAM, *Selections from the Correspondence of Admiral John Markham*, Navy Records Society (London 1904).

ROGER MORRISS, *The Royal Dockyards during the Revolutionary and Napoleonic Wars* (Leicester 1983).

The Naval Chronicle Vols I-X (London 1799-1803).

H W RICHMOND (ed), *Private Papers of George, second Earl Spencer*, Vols III & IV, Navy Records Society (London 1924-25).

SIR JOHN BORLASE WARREN, *A View of the Naval Force of Great Britain* (London 1791).

Index

Page references in italics refer to illustrations and captions.